Karina Schelde offers us 'sound medicine' grounded in centuries of factual evidence provided by cultures both indigenous and contemporary. This is an excellent book on the uses of the voice as a healing instrument and I highly recommend it.

~ **Michael Bernard Beckwith**, author of *Life Visioning*

Karina has created a brilliant piece of teaching and service in *Expression into Freedom*, resonating with such clarity and depth of experience. She reaches and touches your inner sense and innate wisdom directly. All seekers of self-awakening, use your voice and let sound be your teacher!

~ **Vickie Dodd**, author of *Tuning the Blues to Gold*

This book and CD offers you the guidance to find the power within you, so you can make the necessary jumps of rapid transformation on your soul's journey. Expression of self is most powerful in sound. This book is a must for everyone interested in making more of their lives and their presence on this planet.

~ **Roy Martina MD**, author of *Emotional Balance*

A book of connecting to the deepest and most sacred parts of ourselves. Written in and easy and accessible language, Karina inspires us to listen with soul and soar with our voice's unlimited possibilities.

~ **Kristin Flood**, author of *The Francis Factor*

Karina Schelde's captivating and beautifully illustrated book will make you sing, dance and laugh! This book is a manifestation of how to change your life, and guides you step by step to discover the huge potential we all have in our innate voice. ~ **Eve Hogan**, author of *Rings of Truth*

Expression into Freedom calls for a shift in human consciousness to align with the divine resonance within us all. Karina inspires with her depth, passion and radiance and is a wonderful reminder of how to sound ...

~ **Gwyn Williams**, author of *The Zen of Touch*

Karina's gift of inspiration allows you to reach your potential of extraordinary depth, connecting your voice and soul as one. With carefully chosen exercises *Expression into Freedom* is a must for everyone on the path to higher consciousness.

~ **Peter Grunwald**,
author of *Eyebody: The Art of Integrating Brain, Eye and Body*

EXPRESSION
INTO FREEDOM

Voice and Sound your Destiny

soul voice®

Karina Schelde
author and founder of Soul Voice®

STEELE ROBERTS | AOTEAROA NEW ZEALAND

Soul Voice™ is a trademark of Soul Voice International.
National Library of New Zealand Cataloguing-in-Publication Data
Schelde, Karina.
Expression into freedom : voice and sound your destiny /
Karina Schelde.
Includes bibliographical references.
ISBN 978-1-877577-87-1
1. Sound—Therapeutic use. 2. Voice—Therapeutic use.
3. Mental healing. I. Title.
615.83—dc 23

Photography: Phillipa Karn, info@phillipakarn.co.nz
Cover design: John Cathro, anjo@clear.net.nz
Graphic design: Matthew Bartlett, Steele Roberts

CD included with Soul Voice™ Practices
Speaking voice and sounding: Karina Schelde
Music and sound engineering: Kevin Clark

STEELE ROBERTS PUBLISHERS
BOX 9321 WELLINGTON, AOTEAROA NEW ZEALAND
info@SteeleRoberts.co.nz • www.SteeleRoberts.co.nz

Contents

Note: Exercises are in italics.

*To my ancestral roots
and the Soul Voice Community.
To all my students, who have been
the inspiration behind this book.
To all human beings who are called to awaken
the wisdom of their voice.
To my spirit guides, Mother Earth
and Father Sky, for guiding me
in my teachings to humanity
to make a difference in healing Planet Earth
with grace and in resonance.*

Foreword

Over a number of years I've had the great fortune to experience Karina Schelde's various healing gifts, in California, Hawai'i and New Zealand.

She has helped me realise that the battleground between my heart and my head resides in my throat. This tug-of-war between romance and reason meant that I often found my voice lacked a natural confidence. Over the course of working with Karina, I've found a powerful voice full of intuition and truth. I'm not sure how she was able to coax it out of me, but I do know that the exercises that she has outlined in this book have changed my life. And, ironically, after more than two decades as a CEO, I now use my voice in my profession as an international speaker.

No matter what your profession is or where you are in your life, you will find Karina's guidance in connecting with your inner voice to be profound. I am so impressed with this book: not only the content, but also the graphics and the exercises that make it such an enjoyable read and an opportunity for powerful self-reflection and development.

For many of us, our voice and breathing define the state of our life. They truly are a gauge of our inner wellbeing. Letting an emotion move through you is healthy. Letting an emotion define you is not. With this book, you can explore your emotions and your voice to navigate difficult or unknown terrains, and Karina is masterfully helping you climb these emotional peaks and challenging valleys.

Expression into Freedom is an opportunity to tap into the power we all have in our voice — the one that authentically represents why you're here on this earth.

~ **Chip Conley**, founder of Joie de Vivre Hotels
and author of *Emotional Equations*

Acknowledgements

My long-awaited book has been birthed to complement the *Soul Voice* book.

I have chosen some of my favourite pictures from Soul Voice® training sessions to enrich the content and I am deeply grateful to all the students who gave me permission to use these images.

The case stories from certified Soul Voice practitioners are a rich addition; I give my heartfelt thanks to all of you for writing your stories with such clarity, determination and joy of expression.

Thank you to all my Soul Voice students, practitioners and teachers for the huge inspiration you have been for this book; I receive so abundantly from witnessing your in-depth processes and your commitment to the work.

A special gratitude to those key people worldwide who support the Soul Voice organisation gracefully and with such integrity and passion. Your priceless gift is indispensable to me.

To my friends and family around the globe I express my gratitude for all your love and care, which is so precious and essential in my life and healing work. Thank you so much.

My sincere gratitude to Chip Richards, who once again helped me sculpt and structure a new book.

To Philippa Karn: your skilful photography has been an extremely rewarding experience for me. Thank you.

A special thank you to Chad Beckett for the great photos you contributed.

To John Cathro for helping me with such exquisite graphic design, which is so much an inspiration for this book. Thank you for your ongoing support.

To my beloved husband Kevin, for without your unconditional love and blissful trust in me always, I would not have been able to complete this book.

How to use this book

Expression into Freedom is an invitation to dive deeply into the voice that remembers *you*, but which you may have forgotten. Using your voice in conscious sounding can access places you might have never before visited. It brings you in contact with the essence of your soul by revealing untapped potential. *If you have a voice, you can sound* and you cannot do it wrong! All expression has a unique message, so listen.

This book is complementary to the *Soul Voice* book and guides you further into the Soul Voice® method.

Each chapter is a universe in itself, so feel free to read the chapters in any order. It is a book that asks you to stop and take

And God said,
'Let there be Light'.
The sacred sound of God's work
created the Light
and so it is ...
we are the sound of all creation.

breaks often. The array of pictures have their own language and communication and they support the embodiment of the written word with more ease, flow and joy.

The book is an invitation to become more conscious of dormant patterns or a lifestyle that doesn't serve your highest integrity any more. Let yourself be surprised!

Take responsibility for what you learn, and seek help from a professional Soul Voice practitioner if needed. The exercises cannot replace hands-on therapeutic voice work, but practising them on a regular basis will support rejuvenation, release of stress and pains, and will accelerate your overall wellbeing, health and playfulness. The book also includes short exercise-surprises called *Try this,* a treat for the soul in action.

Get out of your own way and surrender to the outcome. Let go of high expectations and be passionate about your progress and discoveries as you let the sound itself be your guide. Remember you are never alone in your practices. The more you love yourself and dedicate yourself to the highest good of all, the stronger the ripple effect around you will be.

An instructional CD is included. Allow *my voice* to support you and have the courage to persevere with the Soul Voice medicine. May it inspire you to explore the method further.

CHAPTER 1

The human voice
as ultimate expression

*There is a longing in human beings to fully
open up their voice, to communicate the truth.
There is a cry deep within our hearts
that wants to be heard, a longing to
free our greatest potential through the voice.
It is the most powerful tool available
for the healing of humanity and
in significantly shifting consciousness.*

Humans are resonant beings

Our voice remembers what we have forgotten. It reveals a richness, aliveness and power, our light and dark sides. It carries any suppressed or painful memories and indicates our spiritual path. It is our vibrational blueprint and a living testimonial of who we are in a soul essence. All we have to do is to stop and listen to its vibration — to be still, so we may intuit and feel what the sound and the tone of voice is telling us. When we are still, our being becomes more clear, vibrant and pure. The voice is an authentic messenger, it never lies. It reveals a universe of moods and emotions, history and stories, desires and tensions, thoughts and hopes. The voice has a precise and distinct character, which can connect or distance us from a person.

The human voice is the most powerful and effective of all instruments, because it has soul and higher consciousness. Virtually every known indigenous culture has used the healing power of sound medicine for eons, practising and honouring sound as the fundamental creative force of the universe. Everything is made up of vibration and frequency. We are held together by sonic resonance, and each part of our body has its own sonic vibration. Therefore, any part of a person which is out of balance (experienced as pain, fatigue, distress or hurt) can respond effectively to healing with sound. From simple discomforts to deep-rooted problems, sound simply heals.

Our vocal expression cannot be freed without taking care of the emotions, as they ultimately conduct our subconscious reality and vibrational equilibrium.

The voice is the key to exploring our creative power and the potential of our multilayered sub-personalities, which are a rich reservoir of roles we play in life. When we take the challenge to move into the subconscious, the sacred medicine of our innate voice will come forward and soar in remembrance, showing us the way.

Emotions are a bridge that unites body, mind and voice. Emotions connect our soul and subconscious, the internal web which holds us together. Without working consciously with the emotional body, our vocal healing ability and our expressions remain restricted and limited.

Sound and science

In the 1960s Swiss scientist Dr Hans Jenny corroborated ancient knowledge in his book *Cymatics*:

> Sound has a direct influence on our human biology and thus influences our health. This is because every cell in our body has its own vibrational frequency. Human cells are composed of atoms and molecules that resonate according to their mutual harmonies. Many cells together form tissues and organs that are part of a biological system. This system then vibrates according to new harmonies ... Sound is the creative principle, and must be regarded as primordial.

Quantum physics tells us that the whole universe is made up of vibrational fields of energy. Recent research by a team of Danish scientists shows that our nerves do not transmit electricity, but they in fact transmit sound; thus sound frequencies are embedded in our nervous systems. Each individual human being has their own unique frequency that will vary depending on our emotional, mental and physical state of being.

If we sprinkle fine sand on a drumhead and make vibrations by sounding harmonious frequencies, the sand will progressively create *sacred geometric patterns*. Sounds can move energy and cause changes in the molecular structure. This means that we can change any structure through sound frequencies, if the resonance matches the structure and the intention.

Therefore we can change our state of being at any given moment by tuning into the sound frequencies needed for the intended outcome. We can choose the vibration from within and use our own voice and sound to correct any mood, condition, blockage or illness.

The loss of connection to our true voice

As babies we were strongly in contact with our senses and primordial language (see Chapter 2), and through sound we were in tune with organic life, our emotions and pure vibration. As we grew up we closed down our spontaneity and innate imagination and potential. The intuition we experienced as children became diluted or severed by limiting thought and belief patterns. Our emotional being eventually suppressed or shut down.

Our world today is causing many people to live out of balance. We have lost contact with nature and with our original innocent selves. We have lost contact with the part of us that resonates with

Everything in nature is a print of sound creating form and matter, colours and spirals. Nature exists in sacred geometric constellations. Nature is creation in sound, and so are we.

all living things and with the essence within ourselves. The pace of life is continuously accelerating us to be more effective than ever before, and every day we are bombarded with more information and stimulation than some of our ancestors encountered during their entire lifetimes. Where are we heading? What is the goal in escaping and running away?

When we get more and more stressed and when this imbalance takes over we suppress our natural impulses, our innate spontaneity and our inner child's creative expressions. For many of us, lack of being honest to ourselves and giving space and time to listen to our own needs and desires means that we get intertwined with others' expectations, which may not resonate with who we truly are.

My personal journey and the Soul Voice teaching

One of my first vocal courses, three decades ago at the Roy Hart Theatre in France, was a remarkable birthing process for me. I had previously been trained by opera singers, who did not teach me how to access the soul of my voice, and at Roy Hart I experienced a tremendous freedom through releasing all the sounds and tones that wanted to come through me spontaneously. I had stuffed so much inadequacy into my voice and was terribly afraid of not doing it right, not hitting the right notes. In this training

There may be no more potent way to heal the planet than by awakening our own innate capacities, and using the voice and its many creative expressions as a healing medium through all the systems of our own body — mental, emotional, physical and spiritual.

In bypassing linear language and communicating in sound language we are brought into places so deep there can be no description in words.
Because we consist of vibrational energy, our sounds are an accurate blueprint and synergy of who we truly are in this present moment.

I could allow my intuitive voice to make absolutely any sounds, many of which originated from long-suppressed emotions and inadequacies. They all became transformed into blissful sounding. I sang notes on the scale and notes off the scale. There was no judgment; it didn't matter. I experienced that what is behind the voice is what counts: my dedication, my presence, my emotions, my willingness, my heart.

A life-changing initiation brought me on the sound and voice path: I was working on this auspicious day with a client I already had seen for several coaching and bodywork sessions in my healing centre in Denmark. One day, as I was working with severe pain in her abdominal area, which I previously had not been able to resolve through hands–on healing and counselling, sounds started to pour out of me. They came from everywhere, and they took over completely and guided me. After a short while the pain was gone. A period of silence and deep inner listening followed, where the root cause was revealed to me, as I continuously listened to the new frequencies of my client's body. After this experience my personal journey into sound and voice work was born. It was my vocation.

Since that day in 1988 I have been guided to bring a creative, therapeutic voice healing modality to humanity, the Soul Voice® method. This honours the ultimate expression and potential of our unique human voice. The voice remembers the ancient wisdom coded in our cellular memory and teaches us how to cultivate and evolve our intuition and higher consciousness. I build structures to channel the information that wants to come through in a more grounded form, which then becomes tangible and effective for people to work with.

I guide the human voice according to my intuition and its own cellular memory. From that place I listen and respond to the recipient's consciousness and impulses, and hear what is most essential and needed in the evolution of the voice and consciousness. I teach how to go to the core of an issue through a reprogramming process of unravelling the emotional layers which hinder the issue from being fully resolved and healed. The Soul Voice method engages a full spectrum of physical, emotional, mental and spiritual exercises and techniques, which enable each person to develop their own unique creative vocal expression and boundless potential. Only by listening to our true nature can we be reborn again and again, and play our part in the cosmic symphony. Only by creating a strong individual voice can the collective energy grow accordingly

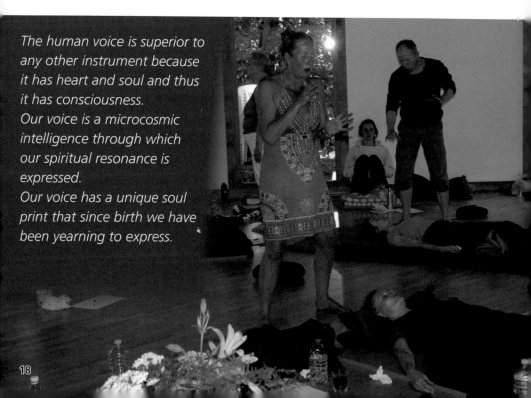

The human voice is superior to any other instrument because it has heart and soul and thus it has consciousness.
Our voice is a microcosmic intelligence through which our spiritual resonance is expressed.
Our voice has a unique soul print that since birth we have been yearning to express.

Freeing your innate expression will set you free. By unleashing and experiencing the untapped power of our voice we liberate our whole being and limitless creativity; we awaken our authentic and playful self.

and coherently. I am passionate about teaching and sharing my service with humanity. It gives me the greatest self realisation and it pushes me to stay on a dedicated, uncompromising path of truth and freedom.

Our greatest barrier to not living life fully is our lack of being in complete acceptance of *where*, *who* and *what* we are. We pretend, we judge, we make ourselves better or worse than we are. We hide behind a title or a name, being 'somebody'. We react, we procrastinate, we are scared of breaking out of our habits and taking the leap. How will life be without all these labels? How will life find *you* in all these shadows?

We are afraid of being seen, honestly heard and truly loved. We hide, not receiving life one hundred percent. We shortcut our breath, our life urge, our passion, our joy, to fit into expectations, distractions, demands, and duties.

I thrive on taking jumps, quantum leaps. It wakes me up to flow with the unknown, and it shakes the dead branches off 'my inner trunk'.

Sound is one of our greatest doorways into the creative power of the subconscious mind. The voice itself is the teacher.

Who am I not to take the risk and challenges in these fast-moving times? It makes me so alive and it stretches me to be on the edge. At the same time I navigate a safe path, because I know what and who I am, and especially who I am not to be. *The unknown becomes knowingness when we follow that divine spark of inspiration, when we live the present moment fully, no matter what it takes or how great the fear is.*

The feeling voice

When our words cannot express what we are feeling, a new song is born; it is then we may spontaneously open to our natural expression in sound. In ancient times people gave sounds to their body language. Men and woman sang to express their emotions before they were even able to speak their thoughts.

Our emotions will become the bridge to our sensuous being and to our subconscious, when we allow ourselves release from being static, habitual, stuck or numb. Emotions are the gateway to both the spiritual and the physical world. We need to burst and rise in our emotions. Our hearts need to open to have the ecstatic experience of what it really means to live. If we ignore this vast immeasurable experience we call emotions, we become half-dead in both our voices and in our bodies. Our consciousness needs to be fed by the emotional body in order for the inner voice and our guidance to become authentic, real and embodied. Our voice

cannot reach its fullest potential without working in-depth with the emotional body.

Our emotional state of being continuously influences our thought processes, our consciousness and our body's chemical and biological structure. Think how different our day would be, if we were not covered by a veil of unexpressed emotions, but instead were full of joy.

Without taking our emotions seriously, we are not able to play authentically. When our emotions are owned and expressed, they become the key to happiness and aliveness. They are transformational shape-shifters of our personal make-up and vibrational print.

We are not only what we think: *We are what we feel — and we become what we express!* Our nerves, originating from our spinal cord, tell us that we are indeed emotional beings. When we sigh, laugh, cry, groan or moan we release our mental controller, and we start to feel.

➡ TRY THIS:

» Make a sighing sound and allow yourself not to control or hold onto it.

» Practise several sighing sounds and eventually let it develop to an *ah*-sound. Take a full deep breath and express an *ah*-sound, as if you are almost tasting it. A simple *ah*-sound is such a wonderful heart-opener.

» Remember, sighing sounds or a couple of *ah*-sounds may create a little miracle of release of stress and tension at any time.

» Make sighing sounds or *ah*-sounds while reading this book, and notice how the flow of reading becomes easier.

It is not possible to express a false note or a wrong sound. Each sound is a perfect expression of who you are, and every sound and every expression carries a unique message for you.

Be the change you wish to see in the world

*F*or each experience we go through in life, the body keeps memories which are like records of encoded sound frequencies. We are sound vibration. From this precious truth, what a universe we have to explore! What an unlimited gift there is in the human voice to 'know thyself'. What a reservoir of mystery and unknown potential to be revealed. The power of our true voice resides in our soul, and can be activated and ignited through spontaneous sounding and creative expressions. Voice and sound your destiny. Give voice to any situation that needs to change and be uplifted. Give voice to your activities and become a resonant sounding board for your surroundings. Express what bothers you or hinders you in becoming present to the now. Allow yourself to be true to yourself and let your inner child soar in vulnerability; play with creation. Let go, to become the web without the weaver. Be one with your expression. Share with others to raise your individual strength and commitment, that others may soar and fly in your presence!

*Be the change you wish to
see in the world.
Nobody can do it for you,
so take action.
It is you we are waiting for.
The calling is yours.
Each day is a new beginning,
a journey of soul-felt
expressions. So live it!
Let go of suppression,
hesitation, procrastination.
Express your freedom
to be heard, to be FREE.*

CHAPTER 2

Primordial sound
is the original language

To be heard is our true nature.
To sound is to come back
to the original language,
where everything begins and exists.
To awaken the primordial self
touches the very core of our being,
which is beyond separation.

Diving under the surface, suddenly I can hear him in the distance, his hauntingly peaceful hymn, echoing through the water, moving to and through me. Up for air and I see his breath plume up on the horizon as well. I dive back down to listen. This ancient song that has circled the globe for millions of years. This song that continues to change and evolve, yet is sung in unison by all within a thousand miles. This song that unifies and guides the way of all who hear and join its chorus. It has been said that the song-lines of whales weave a sonic web of energy through earth's waters — that the frequencies and vibrations of their singing actually helps to keep the magnetic fields of our planet in balance. As the pulse of this humpback sonnet encircles me, I feel the truth of his song-line to the core of my being. And I find myself wondering, how can I — how can we begin to access the primordial energy of our own voice in such a way that it contributes to the balance and the harmony of life — in our own bodies and in the living body of our Planet?   ~ **Chip Richards**

Primordial inheritance

In my research it has been essential to honour and to cultivate the origins of our existence through primordial sounding to experience the full spectrum of the Soul Voice work. We are primordial beings, originating from the animal kingdom; we are linked to animals through our instinctive power and conscious communication in sound language. Humans are the only species that does not have a sound language, a unique cry and call. But we can find it.

Immersing ourselves in nature may bring instinctive energy into perspective. When I am merging myself with the elements, I sense a primordial belonging and connectedness, when listening to the sound of the wind and exquisite birdsong, or when experiencing the ocean waves crashing on an endless shore.

Sound existed before language and was our original form of communication. Hearing is the first sense that is developed in the fetus. Only four months after conception, the sense of hearing is fully developed. Sound is absolutely vital to the newborn baby,

Primal sound makes us feel immediately connected; it gives a sense of coming home, maybe a sense of being in an immortal soul-body.

just as primordial sound is highly important for its development. French scientist Dr Alfred Tomatis says:

> The vocal nourishment that the mother provides to the child is just as important to the child's development as her milk.

Neuroacoustic researcher Dr Jeffrey Thompson says about primordial sounds:[*]

> Our first sensory experience in life as a fetus in the womb is of sound and vibration. We float in body temperature amniotic fluid — weightless. We have fluid in our nose and mouth, which eliminates the senses of smell and taste. We have our eyes closed and are in the dark, no sense of sight. We have fluid in our ears pressed right up against the eardrum, but sound travels through water five times more effectively than through air, therefore our sense of hearing is actually amplified. The symphony of sound patterns we experience at this time will be deeply embedded in our subconscious mind for the rest of our lives, the sound of water swishing, arterial pulse sounds and voices. These are our first experiences of primordial sounds.

* Dr Jeffrey D. Thompson, Director of the Center for Neuroacoustic Research, Carlsbad, CA, USA. www.neuroacoustic.com.

Furthermore Dr Thompson speaks about recording people speaking by speeding up or slowing down their speech:

> It is interesting that recordings from the human voice should sound like nature sounds. What happens if we take cricket sounds and slow them down? They sound like birds chirping. Bird sounds slowed down sound like dolphins, and dolphin sounds slowed down sound like people singing. It's almost as if the whole universe is one organic being with many parts all designed from variations of the same blueprint.

The gift of the tongue

I get great joy from watching a baby have fun exploring sound language and its many intricate expressions of the tongue. They can show us our inner child's playfulness and innocence; the part of us that is in closest contact with our essence.

The tongue shapes our speech, sounds and resonance. It is an organ of the greatest flexibility and expansion, able to move in nearly every direction as it articulates.

I have researched the various subconscious layers that we seem to have lost since infancy, and have created a series of evolving primordial 'baby sound exercises'. They are specific practices that have developed into an effective way to get us to surrender control, release tension in the tongue and the larynx, and to listen to our own origins.

When I first presented the baby sound exercise decades ago to my students I got all kinds of reactions, even though I had made the exercise very safe and non-threatening. Some of the students were so shy and inhibited that they didn't want to do it. It's very revealing to expose your tongue, pull it in and out of your mouth, but it is playful and can be practised with lots of ease, flow and humour.

In daily life I usually utilise spontaneous primordial sounds, not only with the intention of spontaneous release to stay in exhilarated aliveness and awareness, but also in my weekly bodywork session. No matter where I travel on the planet I aim to receive a weekly massage. As I receive, I naturally breathe deeply and let the breath itself express sounds. My sounds may be groaning and moaning, often guttural and primal. It is an organic process, and it helps me to sink deeper into relaxation, release and listening. At the same time I know that the sounds stimulate most therapists to open even deeper into the tissue and the energy worked with. What a pleasure to acknowledge and delve further into being a primordial

)))) EXERCISE
Primal expression through baby sounds

This exercise will lubricate your vocal cords and open you to innocence and vulnerability. It will also release tension in the tongue and the whole throat area. Practise baby sounds when you have overdone any form of vocal expression, or to ease emotionally charged situations. It is also an excellent exercise to simply relax and let go.

>> Sit in a comfortable position or lie down. Connect with your deep breathing, using your belly muscles, and relax. Make several sighing *ah*-sounds. Be comfortable.

>> Move your tongue back and forth inside your mouth, as you call forward your innocence and playfulness. Think about being a child or a baby. When you are ready, begin to stretch your tongue; be curious about how the tongue wishes to play, undulate and move, both inside and outside the mouth. Play with any sounds which spontaneously occur. If you are shy to open your mouth at first, just play with your tongue with almost closed mouth and let it develop from there.

>> Let go of control the best you can. Enjoy, have fun and be conscious at the same time. Indulge yourself. How flexible can your tongue become? How vigorously will it be able to move? This may provoke laughter, so go with it.

>> If emotions are awakened, trust that this is a part of baby language and its intuitive remembrance. Do not go deeper than you can handle on your own. If necessary, seek professional help.

>> When you feel complete, close with sighing *ah*-sounds. Focus on deep breathing for several minutes. Listen in silence with open or closed eyes.

>> Take time to journal your experience, which will support integration. *Enjoy!*

human being, while enjoying getting the body pampered! I highly recommend you to try this next time you visit your masseur or masseuse.

> Primordial sound is the mystery link that holds the universe together in a web that is the quantum field. ~ **Deepak Chopra**

Indigenous evidence

Indigenous cultures have contact with primal instinctive sounds. They use the healing power of sound medicine and have done it since the beginning of the human species, practising the transformational power of the fundamental creative force in the universe: sound.

Sounds unify their tribal existence. The Aborigines in Australia, who are the oldest living culture on the planet, created unique 'song lines' and by singing these songs they were able to navigate and traverse their vast country.

Native Americans remind us that we have forgotten how to live in balance with the earth. They honour the sacredness of all

*Our tribal connection is rooted
in our DNA cellular memory.
Our ancestors are who we
build our lives upon.
Do we honour that?
Do we even think about it in daily life?
Do we hear the calling?
I watch the sun rising
in the early morning.
My voice starts to sound in frequencies
that complement nature and the
elements that abundantly surround me.
It gives me an experience of
a tribal song, immediately bringing me
into connectedness with my ancestors.
This song resonates in my bones
and brings the vibration of nature
closer to me.
I then listen in silence to this beautiful,
precious and primal song.
I finish in meditation as I consciously send
the essence of this song out to humanity.*

things, and tell us that everything is inter-related and connected to spirit. They live this truth in their speech, in their communication with the land and in their songs calling for peace on earth.

The indigenous Balinese culture is based on rituals, ceremonies and prayers overflowing with devotion and love. They use sound, dance and ritual to link the different worlds and to maintain strong union with their family, ancestors and the creator.

We are being called to listen to the messages from indigenous cultures. In the past we all lived tribally. Our ancestors are the roots to our existence. What is common to all native peoples is that they have a wisdom that may seem mysterious and mystical because it is unfamiliar. They have an instinctive yet spiritual wisdom that has been passed down from generation to generation, a connection to all that is.

I am deeply touched when I hear Aboriginal elder Geoffrey Gurrumul Yunupingu singing in his native language. Ancient roots vibrate in my DNA, and a memory is surfacing. Any time I hear a Native American chant I always get goosebumps and I feel rejoicing in my bones when I hear one of my students, African by origin, express her native sounds and language:

> The Soul Voice journey helped me to heal long-standing patterns in my life and discover my true voice. Although I have African ancestry, I have never really felt connected to it — until that moment in the Soul Voice session. For the first time I could feel the native energy through my sounds and feel my heritage. What an honour!
> ~ **Debra Stowmann**

Recently I talked with Maori elder Makuini Ruth Tai about the relationship between the Maori language and nature. Makuini gave an example of water, which is 'wai' in Maori, consisting of the vowel sounds A (pronounced *ah*) meaning the Light, and I (pronounced *ee*) meaning the Creation. She says:

> Water took on a form so it could walk around. All life comes from the waters and it fills me with deep gratitude, even though on a

human level we are still trying to sort ourselves out. The water knows so as we tap into water by being in nature, the genius in us will come out. The water remembers. 'Wai' also means 'song' in Maori, and we grew up filled with singing; everywhere we went we sang! Through song and sound we can express every emotion.

Coming back to indigenous cultures gives me a sense of home and belonging, a sense that their roots are indeed anchored in my DNA. I remember these sounds somewhere in the inner medicine wheel of my life cycles and I rejoice in them. When I visited Vanuatu, in the South Pacific, I planned an adventure in the bush with some indigenous people, not knowing what to expect: Eight dark-skinned men of various ages, dressed in foliage only, were suddenly approaching me with their wild primordial sounds, armed with spears ready to attack me! Their expressions were menacing and purposefully threatening, but I knew I had bought into this experience! It felt real and I had absolutely no fear. What touched me was their instinctive expression, which was authentic and spoke from a real power of expression. They used a sound language connected to ancestral roots, so I surrendered as I allowed myself with enjoyment to be moved.

When you allow yourself to be primal and instinctive, your spiritual qualities get a stronger and more solid foundation to anchor themselves into.

Primal animal spirit

Animals represent our instinctive awareness and primordial nature. Animals are alert and respond to external and internal changes immediately. A part of the human brain is the reptilian brain, which connects us to instincts and sensations, to our primal and gut feelings, a powerful ally when linked to spirit. Our instinctive alertness is often dormant, keeping us from being able to fully be in the present moment, as our rational brain is overriding us with fear and over-control. Thus we lose our connection to impulses and natural instinctive information, which progressively diminishes the power of the reptilian brain within us.

No matter how highly evolved humans become in terms of our abilities to reason, feel, plan, build, synthesise, analyse, experience and create, there is not substitute for the subtle, instinctual healing forces we share with our primitive past. ~ **Peter A. Levine**

Working with the medicine of power-animals awakens the instinctive energy of alertness and awareness and teaches us to reclaim a stronger sensuality and connection to the earth. It may also give us a jump-start to live more strongly in the here and now. Each power-animal of its kind represents a 'kingdom' in itself. For example the medicine of badger represents fearlessness through indomitable courage and willing to fight for what it wants. It helps us to take action in the now, and not procrastinate.*

I use to be afraid of the darkness and unable to walk alone in the forest by night. I winced at rustling leaves, benumbed by every little noise and expecting danger in the shadows of the trees, but I loved nature and felt held back from my needs.

Ready to go through this fear, I walked warily into the nearby forest. Kneeling on all fours on wet earth I called upon the power of the wolf. I asked for its wisdom, its courage and its connection to the earth. In this innocent condition I imitated wolf sounds, at first low, then louder and courageous. I felt the ancient power in my pelvis and the wolf essence inside of me. The sounds permeated through me, giving space and transforming fear into trust. They released me from an old pain. There was no more separation; I became part of the whole. In this state I was able to listen and surrender to the dark, knowing that I had been received. A serrated branch transmuted from a grotesque face into a guardian angel. All those dark trunks were no longer hiding-places for danger, but instead protective shields.

Since then, the wolf has been a faithful companion in my life. He guides me to take leaps in the dark, reminds me to follow my intuition and encourages me to live as I was meant to live. Born to listen and born to be heard! ~ **Miriam Helle**

---

* More power-animal medicine and exercises are described in the *Soul Voice* book

EXERCISE

The primal animal within

This practice will strengthen your instinctive expression, sensuality and earth power. It infuses you with a stronger sense of self, rooted in a primordial essence. It also encourages being playful and adventurous.

» Sit in a comfortable position and make some *ah*-sounds or sighing sounds for a couple of minutes. Contact the lower part of your body and hip area; sink into this area with your awareness as you make more *ah*-sounds. To sense a stronger connection to the earth energy, gently move into an all-fours position.

» Make guttural and growling sounds. At first it may feel awkward. Think how a lion or a tiger would sound and imitate them. Try not to control the sounds that want to come forth; let them flow, knowing that those guttural sounds connect you more strongly to earth power and your instinctive nature.

» You may visualise your chosen animal. Sound like a wolf, a tiger or a panther or any other animal which has some kind of growling-earth sounds. The animal may come towards you, as if it wants to be a part of you or maybe communicate something to you.

» Play with being identified with the chosen animal. Allow these primal sounds to develop as you free yourself into spontaneous body movements. You may also play with imagining your animal in various situations; for example, protecting territory, eating, sleeping or hunting. Have fun!

» Whatever your sound experience is, trust it. Continue till you feel satisfied and fulfilled by these new fulfilling primal sounds.

» Sit in silence and listen to the energy you have just expressed. Receive insights about what it means for you to be in your instinctive power and alertness. Give thanks to the sound itself that flowed through you.

» Journal or draw the experience to support this integration process. *Enjoy!*

Whale and dolphin medicine

For millions of years dolphins and whales have shared their songs. Whales are known to have been here 150 times longer than humans* and have the largest brain of all species on the planet. We are asked to listen to these enlightened teachers of the ocean. As we tap into our primordial existence in sound frequencies, we may start to unravel our own ancient history, which is a part of the ancient mystery of the whales. The teaching is one of surrender. As we allow ourselves to be transformed by listening to our own unique frequencies, the whale's medicine may talk through us to awaken these lost memories.

I invite you to listen and to honour their existence, by listening to them through the ether or from a recording. In the Soul Voice work whales and dolphins are part of the primordial teaching, helping us to connect more strongly to our spirituality and the

* See Scott Taylor's book *Souls in the Sea*.

voice of truth and freedom. I invoke them in all seminars I lead. In humbleness I hear their presence and messages. I allow myself to be sung to by them when I am tired, in doubt or not able to focus on what is most essential.

➡ **TRY THIS:** In your own living room listen to their songs from a recording. Go on an inner journey as you listen in deep relaxation to their teachings and messages. Let them open you and bring you further into your being. Take time to ground when returning.

➡ **TRY THIS:** Explore your primordial essence. It is closer to you than you may think. In some martial arts, for example karate, practitioners express sounds to add power and focus to their effort.

> » If you go to a gym, experiment with exaggerating the sounds you spontaneously express when exercising.
> » Or, in your daily workout — be it yoga, dancing, a stress-management programme or simple stretching exercises — add any kind of spontaneous primal sounding.

» In lovemaking do not hold back these raw primal expressions, which when released will add greater pleasure, fun and endurance.

» Treat yourself to a day at the zoo. Listen to the animals, your primal ancestors. Listen to and explore the various animal languages. Be sure your inner child is alert.

» Go out in nature and be infused by its primordial energies. Find a place that has mud and play with 'painting' your entire body with it, a real treat! You will feel so rejuvenated and connected to Mother Earth afterwards. Live your primal urges!

We carry an inherited wisdom of knowingness. A primal and ancestral remembrance of wholeness is imprinted in our cellular memory, in our own innate voice. If we listen closely to the frequencies of dolphins and whales, we may realise that they are the proof of that knowingness and wholeness.

I am on a stunning black-sandy beach in Bali. The sun is baking hot and there is no one around except my beloved husband Kevin, with whom I am enjoying some privacy. After a long swim I get completely taken by the spirit of the black sand. I roll around as I daub myself with the intoxicating sand until it covers my entire body; I am now totally black. I must look like a native! In any case my sounds take over, accompanied by a strong primal gut feeling. I can't stop laughing, playing, releasing, sounding, into the core of my being. I feel ecstatically filled with primordial spontaneity and a unique beauty. I am so alive, wild, dangerous in a good way and my husband is watching me with intrigue and approaching me with a willingness to play.

CHAPTER 3

The art of listening

When we go to that inner place
of listening and are able to exclude
unnecessary distractions,
then the voice of our soul
will know how to truly receive
and listen again.

I sit in the early morning overlooking a rice field outside Ubud, Bali, listening to nature's symphony. Listening to the sounds of small cascading waterfalls in the garden, squirrels jumping from one coconut tree to another expressing their sounds, cicadas sharing their high frequency sounds mixed with bird calls; a choir of true delight! I start to imitate their sounds or rather make my human sounds in response to theirs. As I further extend my listening, I hear hens making their territorial sounds and a strong wind rushing through the branches of the bamboo.

As I listen further, I also hear motorbike sounds. I realise that they are not disturbing my inner silence, rather merging with nature's harmonies. I sense that my inner focus and centredness is naturally creating a protective field around me; I am able to let go as I choose the sounds I wish to become a part of. I continue my writing, undisturbed and embraced by nature's resonant support.

The art of listening

In asserting ourselves and achieving all that we think has to be done, we often race through our conversations with others without taking the time to connect and genuinely listen.

The Chinese symbol for *to listen* reveals a deeper perspective. The left side of the symbol represents an ear. The right side represents the individual who is listening. It is composed of you the listener, your eyes, your undivided attention, and your heart.

Dr Alfred Tomatis, a French scientist who devoted 50 years to understanding the ear and its function, says:

> The ear is the most important of all of our sense organs. The ear controls the body's sense of balance, rhythm and movement and is the conductor of the whole nervous system. Through the medulla, the auditory nerve connects with the muscles of the body. Hence muscle tone, equilibrium, flexibility and vision are affected by sound. Through the vagus nerve the inner ear

connects with the larynx, heart, lungs, stomach, liver, bladder, kidneys, small intestines and large intestines.

Hearing is highly underestimated in our western society, as 80% of our consciousness goes into our visual perception, our sense of seeing. We can change this by starting to honour our hearing and listening as much as we honour our vision.

Now, take a deep breath, and let that breath bring you into your heart, the centre of your body. Listen and breathe for a couple of minutes as you read on. It is possible to consciously breathe and listen at the same time as you read this book. How extraordinary is that! This is where the inner and the outer world start to merge. I recommend you keep on practising this as you continue to read.

Listening slows us down and confirms *there is no rush*. This is not always easy, as we often habitually misuse the art of listening. Most people are focused on moving faster to be more efficient. I challenge myself to stop and listen. I listen to what my body needs instead of being greedy or habitual in my choices. I pause in a phone conversation to listen for a moment and respond more authentically. I pause when my heart is calling for a couple of minutes of silence by closing my eyes.

What do you do to slow yourself down? Is there something scary about taking a break? If so, do you know what that could be? Why do we not take breaks more often, when we know that doing so is such an energy booster? We have forgotten how to listen to the body's impulses. Our mind's inexhaustible demands have taken over, thus we have lost the innate connection to listening.

When we give time and space to listen, everything starts to fall into place in divine timing.

With my sensitive system I know that if I don't listen I simply start to feel unwell or have a sense of not belonging. Lack of belonging or feeling separated always starts with not being at home in ourselves, which actually means not listening. If we ignore our inner voice and inner knowing too often, we become numb and a slave to circumstance. Living a habitual and comfortable lifestyle is not likely to enhance and expand our listening skills.

Listening is truly an art form, particularly when we listen before we express and communicate our thoughts. Listening brings us into introspection and reflection, as we become fully aware of ourselves. How willing are we to listen when a situation asks for it? Do we know how to listen? *How we respond in a conversation does not depend on how intelligent we are but how we actually listen.*

Every cell in our body is an ear, is a listening cell. We have the opportunity every moment to listen with our entire body.

Listening creates confidence and trust in ourselves, and an awareness of the person we are listening to. Listening is about our yin energy, the part that draws us inward and slows us down so we are able to relax. Listening is about willingness to receive. Listening is a place of surrender and becoming a listening instrument with all of your self.

➡ **TRY THIS:** Ask yourself these questions before reading on:
   » Do you feel it is safe to be in contact with yourself at any given moment and to listen? Are you constantly depending on outer stimuli to feel safe and happy?
   » Are you stressed about achieving something that your inner balance can't cope with?
   » What is it that is hindering you from stopping and simply listening?

» As you ask yourself these questions, you may discover how well you actually take care of yourself. Does that resonate with you?

» How do you rejuvenate yourself so you can be at peace and not preoccupied with the outer world or what is expected of you?

Surrender the ego and come closer to your heart by asking yourself these questions again and again.

Listening to the sound of nature

Thousands of years ago nature was more a part of everyone's living space than it is now. Even some decades ago our listening was more adjusted to nature. Today's pace of life hinders deep inner listening. Every day we are bombarded with more information and stimulation than our ancestors may have encountered during their lifetime.

Nature is an optimal place to become aware of our listening ability; it is where we find peace and harmony. Nature is where we are called to spend more time to ensure balance. Everything has soul. Nature is living vibration. Here you may be able to hear yourself and come into a natural meditative space.

EXERCISE

Every cell in our body is an ear

A simple exercise to extend your listening ears to become the entire body. This practice is a deepening relaxation; it awakens body sensations and valuable insights through true listening.

» Put on a piece of music you love to relax to, and let it play gently in the background. Lie down on the floor, and relax more by listening to your breath. Make a couple of sighing sounds to relax even more. Let a gentle imaginary breeze warm and soothe you. Start to listen consciously to the music and observe where in your body you hear it. Is it in your tummy? Is it around the ears? Is it in your head? Is it around your heart? Simply notice this as you continue to flow with the music.

» Now, sense your whole body floating on an ocean. Go more into your subconscious and dreamtime, and let your breath guide you. Consciously allow the music to permeate into your entire body as you contact various body parts. If any body parts resist or are numb, simply let them be. Surrender even more as you state aloud the intention: 'Every cell in my body is an ear and a listening cell.' Dwell in meditative listening for extended time.

» When you are ready, open your eyes and come to sitting position. Drink water and journal any insights. *Enjoy!*

➡ TRY THIS:

» Listen to the sound of the rain caressing a tree's branches, experience each drop as a universe of wonder.

» Listen to the rhythm and sound of ocean waves washing over the sand in eternal motion.

» Listen to a tree; let it communicate to you; then respond through your sounds or conscious words.

» Listen to the sunrise and let it sing to you.

» Listen to the colour green in nature. Let it rejuvenate your cells and bones as you stretch your body in spontaneous sounding.

» Listen to an insect; allow yourself silence to be a part of its vibration.

» Listen to frogs and respond to them about what you are feeling.

» Listen to a recently opened flower and praise its existence with your beingness.

I always rejoice when I hear yodelling in the Swiss Alps. These are special sounds that reflect the Swiss environment. The yodellers sound both high and low tones, responding to nature's peaks and valleys. As a listener I feel connected to the land's origins, and the sound ignites my own unique sound language.

Boundary setting

We need to become more aware of the damage to our ears and body from the world's growing noise pollution. Noise pollution in the environment is pervasive and invasive. Do we even pay attention to traffic noise or noise from various electronic devices? Most machinery noise depletes our nervous system, and at a high level it is an even greater threat.

Be aware that being bombarded for a long period of time by very loud noise can cause major damage to the entire system. Tinnitus (ringing in the ears) may be an example of this. It could be a message from your higher self to slow down, to listen and to be gentle with yourself. Allow your listening to be connected with deep breathing as often as possible. Listen deeper in meditation to what the Creator has in store for you. Maybe you have overlooked a vision you were to fulfil, or perhaps you are being asked to listen beyond the ringing to hear even higher frequencies and to surrender to them. Maybe you are being called to listen creatively to your musical abilities and discover that the higher frequencies are a portal for that to happen? Accept and let go of your stress. By employing your deepening listening skills and patience you may, step by step, overcome the disorder — or see it as a gift.

Another form of pollution we all know very well is being exposed to too much chatter. Maybe you are expected to listen to things you don't want to hear about, or maybe you receive too much information by listening for extended hours to the media? Practise discernment, and make your choices to protect your sensitive listening body.

The inner voice

The inner voice is a consciousness, a state of knowingness, an instinctive feeling or an intuitive sensation of being guided by a higher energy. The inner voice is a state of being and of insightful information, which is connected to truth and soul. It is our safeguard, our guide in life.

The inner voice is refined the more we use it; how wonderful is that! I have always lived my life knowing that *God dwells in the*

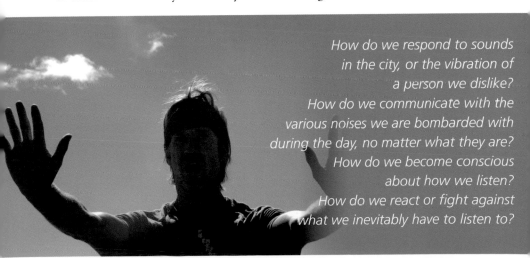

How do we respond to sounds in the city, or the vibration of a person we dislike?
How do we communicate with the various noises we are bombarded with during the day, no matter what they are?
How do we become conscious about how we listen?
How do we react or fight against what we inevitably have to listen to?

Boundary setting with invasive noises

This exercise will progressively support you in excluding invasive noises. It restores boundary setting and a sense of feeling safer within your own healthy boundaries.

» Focus your gaze in front of you, for example on a spot on the wall, a picture, a flower or a power object. Take some deep breaths and start to sound either *ah*-sounds or *oh*-sounds. Make the exhaling sound long.

» Now direct your sound through your body from head to toe with a downward motion, as you let the energy from any disturbing noises be a part of you by accepting them. With the next sound you produce, let it go from your feet into the earth itself, as you focus on completely letting go and composting into the earth any residues of these disturbing invasive noises. Continue this process for as long as needed. You may keep your eyes open while you focus on the chosen object or you may close your eyes at any time.

» Listen to when you have reached a completion; trust your intuition. Focus on deep inner listening to your heart for a couple of minutes. Create in your third eye a sense of the colour violet, and let it sweep around your entire body. Sound the colour violet by feeling it for an extended time. Violet is an effective colour for protection. Let the colour create a clear and firm protective veil around you.

» Make a note in your journal about the outcome. Continue your day in assertiveness and acceptance with an awareness of the violet colour of protection around you. *Enjoy!*

Note: if you are not able to do this exercise with a loud voice, because of the environment you are in, try the same exercise with inner sounds: You do not express the sounds outwardly, but let them intentionally be expressed in silence. You simply visualise the sound you would express by now keeping it within, as a 'soundless sound'. The power of your listening skill and your faith is important here and determines the effect. It will however be helpful if you have first had the experience with sounding aloud.

unknown. For me the name *God* is a natural expression. God is both female and male, an all–encompassing power of wisdom and love, the universe and all that is, a force of a higher consciousness which always knows the highest good.

Do we know our inner voice or do we constantly ignore it, living a busy life or because it is too scary to truly listen? What stops you from following your inner voice? Can you think of a time when you did? What happened as a result? Think about it now.

How do we listen to the inner voice? Where in the body is the inner voice and where in our consciousness? Consider the inner voice being in an area where you feel most at home in your body, a place of surrender and deep inner listening. A place where you can connect with yourself in an honest way. It could for example be in your heart, or in your belly area. Or, it could be in the solar plexus area, the centre of inner power, or in the throat area, centre of expression. I personally never experience my inner voice in my head. The inner voice may also be an overall sensation through the entire body, a sensation of synergy and wholeness, which then may be centred in one particular area of the body. The best way to trust your inner voice is to act on what it tells you.

We so often forget to listen from within, and that is one of the main factors causing stress and illness

If you have a tendency to procrastinate you may not be able to complete a project, or you may be driven by a belief that says, *I will never make it.* Play with the resistance and the obstacle in front of you by making it lighter; be with what you are able to manifest in this moment, even if it is not the whole truth. By experimenting and playing with your options you may succeed in finally making the decision that your inner voice told you to take in the first place. You will be proud of yourself; you made it happen.

Next time you have a conversation with a close friend, either over the phone or in person, try this experiment of authentic listening: let your friend speak without you interfering or interrupting. Dwell within yourself by having the experience of becoming a listening ear with your entire body. When you listen in this altered way, the need for commenting or interfering fades away and you start to listen to the person's tone of voice. This allows the person speaking to feel assured and to speak from a more authentic place, because there is no judgment or need to rush. You create an ambience of complete acceptance; thus you experience knowing much more about your friend, because you listened beyond the words. You came closer to their soul essence, because you gave permission to truly be heard. Simple, yet a revelation.

One night as I was enjoying an exquisite Balinese spa I heard a couple communicating in a way that made me listen intently: he was communicating with his heart and soul, she with her head. She vented one story after another about people's opinion of her and complained about him not listening to her. He was listening with interest and compassion, not trying to lead her away from the chatter, but now and then giving her a loving hug or a caring touch. The scene became significant as it changed: she soon lightened up and communicated from a quite different place within herself. She talked about the peace she now felt, and even became silent. What

Learn by doing it. Following through with what you hear is the only way you can know that it is the true inner voice speaking to you.

a beautiful transformation, as I experienced what listening with soul can do.

The couple left and I was alone in the spa. I started to sound my overtones; the acoustics were so great, like being in a cathedral. My eyes gazed on the many artistic sculptures that curved in all kinds of shapes and figures. I was in a divine primal vortex, where gods and goddesses were woven together among frogs and pigs, monkeys and lizards, flowers and phalluses. What a soul-felt communication going on there; I felt blessed and suddenly couldn't stop laughing.

Follow through on what you hear

Following my inner voice has given me many miraculous and unexpected experiences. It has allowed me to take many quantum leaps by not being concerned about the outcome, and not being attached to doubts, fears and judgments. If I don't take the chance or the risk, I feel I will not move forward; I will limit myself. I use challenges to create a continuous solid foundation for my soul to grow by following my adventurous spirit.

Decades ago I received a very important inner message, which told me I was to leave my home country, Denmark, to spread peace in the world through my travels and teachings. I was walking among the trees on my daily walk in the forest when I heard a voice; it was as if it was speaking to me, aloud and in a physical sense. I listened and understood its message. Something in me was already prepared to take this jump — an inner knowingness almost like a *déjà vu* experience. I frequently get wake-up calls; they give me a sense of not settling for less, and reminding me to aim for what is grander. Extreme challenges as well as gentler ones are worth living for.

How often do you get caught up in habit and settle for less, either in partnership, your work, decision making, where and how to live, or in your choice of friends? Have you ever been habitual for too long in one area of your life? Consider taking a quantum leap and you will most certainly be eternally grateful. We never get more challenges than we can handle; challenges and risk-taking can move us deeply. To know how to listen more deeply, how to follow that inner knowledge, takes courage and faith. Do you have it? Yes you do, but do you act on and use it? That's another story, but it is the main question.

I repeat: the way to trust the inner voice's message is to listen and follow through what it tells you. Only by doing that can you experience living in the divine flow of all things, and respond authentically in your interactions.

It is our birthright to reconnect
with our inner voice.
It is from that place our lives are to be lived
in joy and harmony, and not from our head
or competitive judgmental mind.

➡ TRY THIS:

» Do something you would never consider doing because it feels too risky — for example, jumping out of a plane!

» Take some days off to do activities you would usually not consider. For example, go on a silent retreat, sleep outside under the stars, or go scuba diving.

≈

Illness is the body's way of trying to be heard in a loud way — or, at least, an opportunity to communicate and listen to your cells. When I first met Karina, I could barely walk. A so-called auto-immune disorder, RA, caused my immune system to attack most of the bones in my body, leaving me with inflammation, severe pain, extreme fatigue and deep fear for the future.

I was told by doctors they couldn't do much to help me, that I should only expect the condition to get worse. I tried the many different kinds of chemical medication the hospitals offered me without getting much better; some medicines almost killed me. Finally I received chemotherapy every six months, just to get through the day.

While living this hell I kept thinking there had to be a way to talk my immune system back into reason; that I had the ability to heal myself by talking to my cells. I just couldn't find the language or the voice.

Then I met Karina and the Soul Voice method. I instantly felt that here was the technique that would help me find my way back to myself and the voice that would finally reach my cells. A lot of sounding, emotional releasing, reprogramming, failing and trying again followed in the next four years.

Then came the turning point. One day I had ears, inner ears. My ability to finally listen to my authentic self was a deeply surprising and beautiful experience which completely transformed my life. The moment awakened my ability to truly listen, as every cell in my body happily responded to my deepest intention: *I am healthy.* It took me six years to find my way back to a healthy life, with no pain, no medicine or symptoms of any kind.

When I listen to my body, respect what I hear and respond by mirroring that respect into my sounds and actions, then my body listens to me too.

~ Lolita Bellstar

Silence is dwelling in
sublime vibration of presence.
Silence is the most creative place,
where we simply rejuvenate.
Silence is wholeness, an oasis of
peace and wonder.
Silence is meditation, being in
contact with God beyond thoughts,
feelings or sensations.
Silence is opening up after having a
fulfilling experience.
Silence occurs naturally when we
have lost a close friend or relative.

Silence is when a nation
stops for two minutes or
longer, sending compassion
after a traumatic event.
Silence occurs after a grand artistic
presentation has completed.
Silence is when we go to sleep and
trust the unknown receiving us.
Silence is a universe where all
sounds meet and integrate in a
subtle yet profound way.
That is silence.

Listening to silence

Silence is something we consciously or unconsciously seek all the time. Inner listening gets nourished through *silence*. Taking time off to do nothing and be in silence is such a relief for the whole system.

Silence is an energy of 'beingness' we need to become more familiar with; it trains our subconscious to rest in trust and in peace. If you meditate 30 minutes a day but rush the rest of the day, silence is not a part of your being. You can change your habit any time and you can change it now.

When we start to listen deeply we may be able to hear the voice of a place, a city or any object we are close to. That place or object is encoded with information from the past; when we listen we may be able to access these recorded memories. So it is with the Oracle in Delphi, or Lourdes, for example. The words and the sounds of a saint or a person with great power can thus be received by us. And faith does move mountains! The simplicity of this fact is manifested each time we consciously offer service to our surroundings and to humanity

God's creation is reflected in the mirror of silence and becomes crystallised when we are truly willing to listen.

It is late evening as I listen to the sound of the night, and I feel happy and content. I hear the sound of the village, a pleasant soothing sound that brings darkness and peace. Frogs croak in the pond and I hear an owl in the backyard sending a message: be gentle to your wings and allow them to soar in the dark. A breeze is caressing my hair with gratitude as I close down the computer on the verandah, putting the last lines of my guided information out to the world and into reality.

CHAPTER 4

Emotions are conductors of our wellbeing

Our emotions are like a web
that weaves us into an extraordinary tapestry
towards the infinite.
When the feeling in any given situation
is revealed and expressed,
our voice and creative expression
will flourish, be freed and grow.
We are what we feel.

Emotion and flow

> Emotions are one of the most universal, yet misunderstood, elements of what it means to be human. Get your emotions right and you'll get your life right.
>
> ~ **Chip Conley**, *Emotional Equations*

Emotions are an unfolding heart awareness, which yearns to open to what is not yet known or experienced. Giving yourself permission to surrender to emotional expression will enable every cell in your body to rejoice and rejuvenate. Be gentle yet firm, and persevere to discover emotions as your closest friend. When we lose a loved one or when a natural catastrophe shakes us, our emotional body is stretched and will reveal itself in unpredictable ways. Through exploring the full range of our emotions we become fully present. Emotions are the key to becoming a successful and powerful human being. *If we dare to dive into our many expressions of emotions, we become a truly passionate artist of life itself.*

Could you imagine a world where emotions are missing or not expressed, a world in only black and white? Emotions are the gateway to both the spiritual world and the physical existence. Holding back emotions creates all kinds of aches and pains; when this becomes a habit we may get sick in body, mind and spirit. All blockages and illnesses have an emotional component, and are thus a reminder that we have to learn to deal with emotions.

The heart may ultimately be healed by working with the emotional body

Dr Candace Pert says:

> Emotions are at the nexus between matter and mind, going back and forth between the two and influencing both. All emotions are healthy, because emotions unite the mind and the body. Anger, fear and sadness, the so-called negative emotions, are as healthy as peace, courage, and joy. To repress these emotions and not let them flow freely is to set up dis-integrity in the system, causing it to act at cross-purposes rather than a unified whole. The stress this creates, which takes the form of blockages and insufficient flow of peptide signals to maintain function at the cellular level,

is what sets up the weakened conditions that can lead to disease. All honest emotions are positive emotions.

My research has shown me that when emotions are expressed — which is to say that the biochemicals that are the substrate of emotion are flowing freely — all systems are united and made whole.

If we learn to surrender to body wisdom, the emotion itself will naturally be our guide. Our safety net is our voice. Sounds help the mind to surrender so that we can listen to the emotion and let it guide us, even when it is unfamiliar or scary. If you are able to embrace the fear and own it, the fear will most likely transform quickly by itself.

From a body-wisdom standpoint, being out of mind-control will support the emotions to guide our higher consciousness. This requires giving up letting the mind control the emotions.

Emotions unite seriousness and play. Without taking our emotions seriously we will not be able to play authentically. When emotions are owned and expressed, they become the key to make us happy, free and alive. The only difference between joy and anger on an energetic level is that joy is a much faster and lighter vibration than anger is. Anger is a darker, slower and heavier vibration. When anger is owned and expressed it becomes a very powerful tool to get on with life, and a tool to release procrastination.

*Each emotion has a rhythm
and a life of its own
originating from our cellular memory.
Emotions are the bridge
to our subconscious reality.
As we work with them,
express and transform them,
they guide us into
an altered state of awareness.*

Embrace the emotion

Come to the edge, he said. They said: We are afraid.
Come to the edge, he said. They came. He pushed them and they flew.
~ Guillaume Apollinaire

Emotions are like water, ever flowing and ever changing. The emotion of fear will sneak into us without warning. Collective fear is most often massive and unconscious; it surrounds us with a fog-like energy that often seems impenetrable. Fear carries multi-layered emotions beneath its surface. It is a monster whose eyes are difficult to look into. Don't we often create a protective shell or a false armour around us?

Most human beings have a long list of what they are afraid of — for example, fear of being fully present in front of a group of people, fear of failure, fear of not being good enough, fear of being a success, fear of not eating the right food, fear of not being loved, fear of being hurt, fear of the unknown.

No matter how long your fear list is, fear can be dealt with. It is a moving energy that supports you to delve into all the other emotions, which may be hidden behind fear.

The most important question is how to deal with fear. How can fear be expressed so that it may transform to a higher vibration? How do we 'fake it till we make it'? Own the fear! Give it life as if it was your best friend!

I use a metaphor about fear in my teaching: *Kiss the frog and it will transform into a prince or a princess* — the frog is symbolically the fear. By embracing it, loving it,

If we learn to acknowledge all emotions as being equally important, no matter what vibration they have, we will come to realise that there is always a unique message and teaching hidden inside each of them. By expressing these emotions they will transform to a higher vibration to become whole. We are destined as humans to explore this truth. Living in the expression of our emotional body ultimately brings us back to health and happiness.

kissing it, expressing it, miracles can happen.

Each emotion has a unique quality and has its own vibration. An emotion is ever-changing and cannot be measured; it has its origin in the subconscious, the unknown.

Deepak Chopra says:

> The known is a prison. It is the unknown which is the field of pure potentiality, the field we need to step into.

We are what we feel — our feeling response is what makes us whole. Feelings are always related to the heart. How often have we responded to 'How are you?' by stating, 'Oh, I'm fine,' when we actually don't feel good at all?

You may receive a clear indicator of how you feel, if you start to sound your emotional state of being. Even if it's a feeling that you are less comfortable or familiar with, be courageous! As soon as there is acceptance to allow the emotion to be expressed, you have taken the first step into freedom.

> If I create from the heart, nearly everything works; if from the head, almost nothing.
>
> ~ Marc Chagall

I use the nurture and freedom of nature many times to enhance my emotional body. One day in particular stands out in my memory. I had given myself a few days space to really reconnect with myself by going camping in the Australian bush, near the coast. The ocean has always drawn me towards it, being so vast, connecting and powerful. As I arrived at the beach I noticed the sand and water were completely empty of people as far as the eye could see. I felt as though I had the whole planet to myself on this sunny summer's day.

I felt heavy, full and emotionally charged but sounds would not come right away, so I walked and I walked. My steps got gradually heavier and heavier until I was stomping the sand with much force. Then a sound came, a deep growl from the very depths of my being. This built to a loud yell and the anger came pouring out. I doubled over as if vomiting and I eventually fell to my knees continuing to scream and shout, now beating my fists into the sand and spraying the water high as the waves brought it my way. The solidity of the sand and the effort it took to create dents in it were a great mirror for all the obstacles that continued to get in my way, therefore fuelling my anger.

Nearing exhaustion, the tears flowed and my shouting was reduced to quiet sobbing. I sat with my head in my hands as my shoulders shook. In between the crying I tuned into the soft lapping of the waves and although I felt immensely alone I sensed an element of comfort and ease. I lay down, letting the water flow around me. When the tears subsided I felt pleasantly empty again, held, safe and reconnected.

To care for my emotional body enables me to live fully and be deeply connected to others, living more in the flow, and at the same time being effective in the world, yet in a compassionate way. I am eternally grateful for being able to work with the many layers of my heart.

~ Veronika Busch

Own the fear

Many of our deep-rooted issues are fear-based. Fear often cuts us off from the flow and doesn't let us respond to a situation. Fear may be the first emotion that comes to the surface before we begin to feel the feeling that is hidden within the fear. This suppression weakens the tissues, the immune system and the metabolism.

It is the repressed fear, and the unexpressed emotions beneath the fear, that hinder our creative impulses from flourishing.

We are here on Planet Earth to awaken and to let go, to let our inner light enter the darkest corners of our soul. Ultimately there *is* nothing to be scared of. Fear is an illusion. It is a paradox that one of our biggest fears is the fear of the unknown and therefore fear of letting go.

Acceptance is the turning point to get to know any emotion; to accept, we must cultivate *trust*. Trust that when you are true to yourself you cannot express anything wrong. Have the courage not to hide any longer, or to stop playing a role that doesn't feel right. Trust that emotional expression will serve you to the absolute highest good of all — to become free.

The next exercise will bring you further into the embodiment of trust.

Dissonant sounds, the opener to the emotional body

I have found that through continuous use and exploration of my voice's potential it can produce almost any sound with focused attention. All sounds have to come forward for us to become all that we possibly can be.

Through my research I have found that dissonant sounds are the most powerful and effective way to liberate emotional expression. So, what is a dissonant or discordant sound? It is a sound that you

))) EXERCISE
Accept and trust the unknown

This practice will give you courage to let go of shyness and inhibition, and to vocalise and express any sounds that may be forbidden, or may seem silly. When you play with discordant sounds you have already taken a big leap of trust into the feeling voice.

>> Express your feeling in this moment by letting out any sound. You can always start with a sighing *ah*-sound. Relax gently into letting go. Continue to explore the feeling of the sound; let the sound itself guide you by listening to it, as one sound will lead to the next.

>> Now, sense your whole body floating on the ocean. Go into your subconscious and dreamtime, as the breath guides you. Allow the music to permeate your entire body and contact your various body parts. If any of these parts resist or are numb, simply let them be. Stay fully connected to the feeling of the sound and trust, and accept all sounds that your body wants to express.

>> Now begin to move your body to free the expression even more. Let no judgment or analysis come between you and the vocalisation. Relax and let any part of the body guide you into your next expression. It may sound completely different to what you expect. There may be sounds you do not like, off-key sounds for example. You may express an emotion you did not know you carried. Trust the sound, trust your heart, soar with the expression. Be brave.

>> When you feel complete, allow silence to reveal what it will. Rest and dwell in acceptance and trust. Be proud of how far you went, even if you felt you did not open to the extent you wished. Trust taking this process step by step.

>> Journal or draw the experience to ground the integration. *Enjoy!*

may not immediately like or accept because it has disharmonious frequencies. A dissonant sound doesn't follow the Western scale of being on-key or being in tune.

A dissonant sound assists you to feel real, to go beyond the habitual and controlled you. A dissonant sound may be a spontaneous expression of an emotion, an expression which is not controlled by the rational mind or restricted by how it 'should' sound. It is a sound without limitations and often has an edge of being unusual or less familiar; it can stir you up and feel uncomfortable. A dissonant sound feels especially uncomfortable when it is not owned by the person making the sound.

We are afraid of the unknown, but that is where God dwells. If we could put our fears in the hands of the Creator, our higher guidance, we could change the world overnight.

When we cry, for example, we don't think about these sounds being dissonant sounds, do we? When we give ourselves permission to cry it becomes a natural expression. If we do not accept the expression of crying, we feel stuck. *We cannot express a suppressed emotion without dissonant sounds.* Give it a go and don't try to pretend or be nice; you will miss the point.

Did you express such a sound now? Or did you miss the opportunity to be silly? Remember, it only sounds terrible or feels weird if you do not accept the emotion.

Dissonant sounds are excellent conductors of our emotions. We may be able to heal any condition when embodying our full vocal range and all possible sounds. By doing so we expand our view of life and transform limited beliefs, negative programming and any emotions that hold us down.

When I introduce the concept of dissonant sounds to professional communicators, new heights and depths of their voice register and creative expression are accessed immediately. To work consciously with dissonant sounds is a hidden treasure. The authentic voice will ensure that all sorts of medical conditions start to heal. If you were ever told or believed you could not sing, the discordant sound techniques I use can cure this condition. Not being able to sing on-key or remember a melody is connected to emotional disturbances, often related to childhood memories. Uncomfortable childhood conditions may have built up a feeling of inadequacy in your vocal expression and speaking voice. You may have felt you didn't 'fit in', being an outsider or 'the black sheep of the family'.

The world of dissonant sounds may open you to immeasurable and invaluable new dimensions and hidden layers of your subconscious depths and potential.

My voice and I were on a journey. I searched high and low, constantly doubting my direction — something was missing. Eventually I found Soul Voice and my path became clearer, my vision, voice and world began expanding.

During the practitioner training, difficulties arose. I prided myself on my natural ability to stay in tune with harmonious sounds. I soon realised my voice was 'my thing', my speciality which drew people in and created an instant bond between me and the listener. It was hard for me to break out of that sweetness. Once I unlocked myself from my own prison of 'nice' sounds, my sound journey rocketed forward. Passionately I swam in seas of off-key notes, composing my own scales born out of my own personal intentions, releasing my hurts and worries, permitting full expression of using my own unique voice.

I love my voice. It has taken me a long time to take responsibility and ownership and now I fully embrace and am grateful for my gift. ~ **Anne Marie Hynes**

Expressing our emotional self instead of our controlled self is what it takes. Be innocent and break the inner false conditions which ruin your freedom and natural expression. When we do so we become lighter and more playful. We become less serious and closer to God. We experience freedom and authenticity.

Anger is our hidden power

Anger and grief are our two biggest emotions, anger being a yang and male expression, grief being a yin and female expression. Without knowing the depths of anger and grief we remain restricted and limited.

Anger is hidden power. This is important to know when you embark on facing your anger, because for most people it is such a difficult emotion to work with.

Anger is a cutting-edge energy. You may have experienced a sore spot of anger being triggered in an intimate relationship, or somebody may have stepped over your boundary in a work situation, leaving you feeling disrespected and angry. In the past I initially experienced anger a while after being triggered. Because I didn't know how to deal with anger I numbed myself in the moment, afraid of hurting somebody's feelings or scared of being too powerful in my expression. It seemed already too late or not appropriate; I made excuses so that I could continue to be safe in being habitual, and hiding. Several decades of working consciously and intensively with the emotional body has taught me that we are all vulnerable creatures, who in essence want to heal — we want to become whole. We just need to get support.

Anger cuts through any illusions we may hold on to. When anger is owned it is direct, clear and sharp like a knife or a laser. It is an effective energy that fosters clear decision taking, boundary setting and healthy protection.

Take action from your instinctive self. Ask yourself, 'What does not serve me any longer in my life?' 'What am I hanging on to, although it has no value to me any more?'

Take your first step to do something about it: stand up for yourself and own it, say yes to it. It's in being one hundred percent passionate with such a forbidden emotion as anger so that you will be able to transform it into true power. By owning our anger, knowing its source and taking responsibility for its expression we may be able to use anger's transformative power of positive aggression to move forward.

I love to teach how to deal with anger, because students become so powerful and clear afterwards. When anger has an outlet a new world of trust, compassion and manifestation truly opens. There is probably no other emotion that is as repressed as anger. We have been missing its connection to power. Lack of grounding and lack of contact to reality, manifestation power and a balanced yin-yang energy may be rooted in this deep-seated repressed anger. We have become destructive to ourselves and to Planet Earth, which causes a great imbalance in people and severe pollution to our surroundings.

When we store lots of unreleased power in our system, when we 'sweep things under the carpet' and don't set clear boundaries but procrastinate, anger is knocking on the door. If you are not aware of this, your expression becomes inappropriate anger, loaded with projection. You throw your anger and frustration at situations where it doesn't belong. Do we know this? Yes, we do. Anger is unpredictable when it rages.

Only those who know their own anger, its roots and its origins can rise beyond ego in true manifestation and in true power.

Without saying *yes* to our anger, we cannot reach the peak of our happiness.

YOU are the one who is the director of your anger. You are the one who takes the initiative to stop lolling around and saying all is fine when it isn't.

Without going deeply into our *no*, we will not be able to reach the peak of our *yes*. Setting clear boundaries about what we want and what we don't want is absolutely necessary to stop being invaded by others.

When we are unable to say no *in situations that need a* no, *we allow others to take our power away. This is an important message about leaking energy. If you have such a leak and feel invaded, victimised or sabotaged by others, you can be sure you need to work with your anger. Living victimised in any area of your life can be avoided by working consciously with the emotion of anger.*

When you master anger's reverence and cutting-edge energy it will invite you to look through the illusion, to go to the core of all things and touch the essence of the human psyche. Appropriate anger and positive aggression then become a virtue, a fierce component to move quickly out of stubbornness and procrastination and soar as an awakened manifester.

Grief, the seeds of our light

For the Maori people of New Zealand the tangihanga (funeral ceremony) is the way of managing grief. For Maori, more than for Western traditions, grief is a family and communal experience. A tangi respects the fact that mourning is a process, not a single event, and typically the ceremony will last for three days.

Grief is a natural process and it's such a big healer. Grief is a letting-go process, which brings us to our heart's multi-layered facets. When we are able to surrender and not hold on to our self-righteousness in a situation, we may experience grief. Grief releases our built-up stress, it permeates into hurts we have held on to for too long. Grief melts hurtful memories and unfinished communication: it restores peace to any unbearable situation.

Grief deepens our soul's cellular memory. It touches death, birth and rebirth. Grief is dying into ourselves — it lets us explore

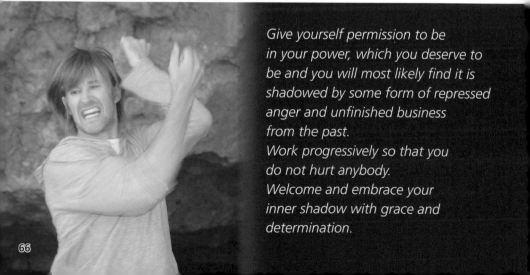

Give yourself permission to be in your power, which you deserve to be and you will most likely find it is shadowed by some form of repressed anger and unfinished business from the past.
Work progressively so that you do not hurt anybody.
Welcome and embrace your inner shadow with grace and determination.

EXERCISE

Anger released

This exercise will help you become conscious of your anger. Anger released brings you back to your authentic power. Among other benefits it may support release of depression, chronic fatigue and chronic pains, substance abuse and weight problems.

>> This exercise may require some vocal warm-up. Take a full deep breath and make an *ah*-sound on the exhale. Do this for a couple of minutes. Then work briefly with the baby-sound exercise (see page 28); let your tongue be loose and flexible, making all kinds of stretches and play. Stay with this practice till you feel open and loose in the throat area and in the whole body.

>> Now get support from 'the primal animal within' exercise (see page 34) to identify your anger. Make sounds on all-fours, as you visualise and express imitating an animal.

>> From that raw state of sounding start to focus on where in your life were you not heard, appreciated or worshipped? Or, simply ask yourself, where do you feel hurt or invaded? Choose one of the memories you are in contact with. Let the sound be your guide. Release the sounds in a downward motion. Stand up and use your feet and hands to let out any sounds that feel good and right.

>> Celebrate your anger and remember, when it's expressed it makes you feel in charge. Consciously use dissonant sounds, let them trigger you and stimulate the process. Use any words that stimulate anger.

>> Express the feeling of being trapped, hurt or invaded. Trust the expression. You may feel inclined to hit pillows with your fists. Bring consciousness into the expression by listening to the sound of the emotion. In this way you combine consciousness and feeling without leaving the charged emotion.

>> If at any moment you sense soreness in your throat, go back to the baby-sound practice.

>> If you feel overwhelmed or not able to focus, stop the exercise and eventually seek professional help to go deeper.

>> Step by step the anger released will transform into powerful harmonious sounding. You may experience richness, fullness, grounding, alertness. Vocalise these qualities for an extended time with the intention of embodying the transformation that took place.

>> When you feel complete, listen to the insights and the qualities of these powerful sounds. Be in silence. Have compassion for yourself and reflect on how to use your new gained power and insights.

>> Journal the experience. Then take a walk focusing on your feet, and walking slowly. Be proud of yourself and what you discovered. *Enjoy!*

the perimeters of our soul. Pictures of Buddha show him with a smile in one eye and a tear of compassion in the other, which tells us he lived in a human body of both joy and compassion.

Tears revealed lead to compassion, as the shedding process opens us to our love and compassion stored beneath our grief. Grief nourishes the soil of our soul's journey. It softens our hard edges, judgments and resistance. It brings us higher consciousness and insights, and its depths of healing cannot be compared with any other emotion.

When did you last have a good cry? Grief is a natural way of letting go, it allows for a more authentic self, it waters the inner garden. When we have a good cry it feels like something has left us; we know we have been in contact with something precious. We feel no longer a victim. We water our soul through shedding the tears which stimulate our biochemistry. Grief can be a hard taskmaster in letting go of attachment. Inevitably there are 'things' we continuously need to let go of, such as positions we did not reach, expectations that left us disappointed, various manipulation games we were not consciously aware of, people we held onto although it was not a healthy or truthful relationship.

Grief is a process teaching us about true vulnerability; grief lets us feel the feeling and is an integral part of healing many issues and illnesses including depression, cancer and heart diseases. Grief makes us feel alive again; grief is for all of us.

A male in his early 30s came to see me about a lower back issue. He said he felt pressure and tightness and it was muscular. He had suffered this pain for over ten years. Upon further questioning he recalled some years back when he was in his late teens, to have been the 'cause' of an accident which led to another person being hurt badly. He carried this guilt and continued to punish himself, and project this on to those around him: 'I'm disappointed in myself,' he said, 'I have made a lot of mistakes, in brief I am irritated and stressed out all the time.'

As I was doing a spinal sound healing treatment, strong sounds of grief came through. My client had a huge release and after his body stopped convulsing, the crying became sobbing. My final sound-scape penetrated into more layers as his body twitched and moved, and the grief released more and more. His own sounds became deeper and more guttural as he connected to his own pain in the spine.

The client told me in the debriefing afterwards that he had experienced lots of walls crumbling around him, that he felt himself open as he let go of the disappointments, judgments and the guilt. He could see purple and green swirling around him. He knew this was a long time coming, he was so grateful he had been given the chance to go so deep. He had never spoken about his feelings around the accident; he had just buried them in his back. He stated he felt such a relief and was now feeling comfortable. 'I see how my environment now has a clearer outlook,' he stated. It was uncomfortable for him to express so many tears, as he had been brought up with the attitude of 'get on with it'!

I saw him in a follow-up session, having giving him practices to work on after the initial session. His pain was gone and he felt ready to start a new life.

~ Lisa Lister

What we have gone through in life and what we may have lost can only come back to us in higher forms when we work consciously to express our grief and hurt feelings.

In ancient times women came together regularly for the purpose of cleansing and releasing. Many indigenous cultures have ceremonies for mourning around various transitions.

Although many men with a Western background have been taught in their upbringing not to cry, there is no rational reason for this, as most men in indigenous cultures do cry. It is about reprogramming, surrendering and willingness to support one another either in group constellations or in relationships to allow grief to be expressed as a natural and constructive process.

Let's cry, not only when we go to a funeral, experience loss or see a movie that touches us deeply, but also as a part of our weekly health programme! Be soft, ease those hard edges where you hold yourself too tight. You will know where it is in your body, or maybe your grief will tell you.

≈

Imagine a grief day for all citizens of this precious blue-green planet; imagine!

Maori leader Makuini Ruth Tai talks about grief and mourning in Maori ritual:

The indigenous culture, the Maori have many rituals pertaining to welcome and farewell. The ritual of the tangihanga or ceremonial bereavement is a time for deepening and understanding our soul purpose. We grew up with death, so it was never frightening. For me death has always been a time of transition. Only the physical dies, the spirit lives on. When someone dies, the tangi [cry] is usually heard. We are able to distinguish the tangi cry above all others. I still can hear clearly my father's cry after he came back from answering the phone when he learned his father had died. I was about nine years old, and his cry pierced my heart. It was normal to grow up hearing men cry. When someone dies it is important to tangi. Everyone is invited to shed tears and release hupe (mucus) and let go of the pain. Songs and chants are sounded to help this process.

I once joined a seminar with 200 other women. My greatest experience at that workshop was a remarkable grief process, where each woman was invited to share her unique grief story. We were to support the person, sharing only with touch and our tears, no counselling, no talk therapy. The way you were asked to best support the process was by accessing your own grief, so that the tribal process could expand and be held safely.

An amazing wave of increasingly profound grief occurred. Many tissue boxes were needed in these hours, where the most authentic stories of violence, abuse, abandonment, rape and failure were shared in 'naked and raw' versions, embraced in deep support and understanding. This huge grieving process became an unforgettable experience of compassion and strong sisterhood.

≈

As I was sitting on the verandah writing about grief, a huge downpour of rain fell from the skies, moistening the earth and my writings! As rain cleanses and clears the air, so does our grief clear our thoughts and soul to be able to receive and give again. It allows the movement of all things to be sacred and to manifest in divine timing.

Grief may be very old and ancestral in our cellular memory, genetically inherited from generation to generation. Grief is a natural virtue of the human constitution. Grief is to be honoured with reverence.

I focus on a flower in front of me and tears come to my eyes. I see and feel that we are all one, we all have grief and tears to share, we are all human creatures with ever-changing emotions. I am touched by all people's differences as not one single soul is the same; not one soul that has the same karma. We all have a unique story to tell, which brings tears to my eyes beyond my understanding.

The power of forgiveness

As I continue to listen to the cleansing rain I touch on the sublime quality of forgiveness. Forgiveness is used in various traditions to stop the suffering from the past, to overcome any held-back emotion, and to restore peace and reconciliation. In any conflict situation or communication where I may feel uneasy, I use the power of forgiveness.

When we have experienced true forgiveness in situations of painful relationship break-up or hurtful projections, our body memory stores these experiences, so next time you forgive it may resonate from an even deeper place within you. You may then truly mean *I forgive,* when you utter it.

Forgiveness requires our detachment. If you hold onto your self-righteousness and projections, it's difficult to forgive. If you

EXERCISE
Grief released

This exercise may become deep very quickly. I recommend that you set a specific time frame to work with this practice; I recommend to start with five or ten minutes. The grief exercise supports you in containing and expressing more of your life urge and joy. Among other benefits it may support release of depression, hypertension, over-eating, heart conditions and lack of commitment.

» Be still and take some deep breaths with sighing *ah*-sounds on the exhale for a couple of minutes. Hold your face in your hands and gently massage your facial muscles. Make sounds, which imitate what grief and sadness is for you in this moment. Let it progressively evolve, as you think about anything you may be sad about; areas in your life, where you have been hurt or disappointed, places where you have attached yourself unnecessarily or maybe a longing you have, which makes you sad.

» Let the emotion flow without having expectation of how it sounds, or what the outcome may be. Be gentle and go slowly, as you keep your consciousness on listening to the sounds at the same time.

» Sometimes five minutes is enough to start to feel a release and a sense of deepening vulnerability; other times you need longer. Trust if you do not succeed the first time you do this practice. I remind you to set a fix time frame, which will support not becoming overwhelmed so you may hold the container of your expression.

» Finish the process with harmonious sounding for an extended time. Focus on a quality that makes you feel peaceful and warm within; a quality of nurturing and caring. Let it assist you in establishing grounding and security.

» Eventually finish with forgiveness-statements you find below.

» Before returning to your activity take time to make notes in your journal or take a walk to integrate the experience. *Enjoy!*

are not willing to let go and empty yourself of past memories and experiences which hurt you deeply, forgiveness will meet resistance within you.

Allow yourself to soften and know that your enemy may be your greatest teacher in forgiveness.

➡ TRY THIS: Read the following statements aloud:

» I forgive myself for all these times that I played being strong instead of showing the strength of weakness and sadness.
» I forgive myself for not expressing my grief and anger.
» I forgive myself for not being perfect.
» I forgive myself for minimising my power and not believing in myself.
» I forgive myself for all my struggle.
» I forgive myself for not knowing better.
» I forgive myself for judging and being misunderstood.
» I forgive myself for projecting my unresolved stuff on to others.
» I forgive myself for not showing up and being honest.
» I forgive myself for not wanting to be heard.

You may continue your own personal statements of forgiveness. Remember, *feeling it is healing.*

> I felt the urge to have a fire ritual on the shore of a lake at a colourful autumn sunset. I started to sound with the first strike of the match. After a while the fire whispered back 'forgive yourself'. I answered to the flames and vivid scenes appeared. Moments when I hide behind my shyness, moments when I judged myself, when I gave my power away, when I did not honour my mother and my ancestors, when I abandoned my inner teacher! The flames slowly retreated but continued to spark in the centre, sheltered by big black logs. My whole attention went to the light of the fire. I was in a temple. There were two monks cleaning a Buddha made of clay, and I remembered a whole story that was told to me a long time ago. The monks dusted the Buddha very carefully and one day they noticed that there was something sparkling from this Buddha. Over the next few days they dusted the Buddha with much devotion. More and more golden spots appeared and sparkled in pure light until finally a whole golden Buddha appeared. The monks went to the head-monk of the temple and told him about the golden Buddha. He remembered that a long time ago there was an invasion in this area; to prevent the invaders from taking away the golden Buddha they covered it with clay. Pure sounds came through me. How much time do I spend with a layer of clay around me and others? How often do I still act out from this? I

had forgotten that I can just tune in, connect and surrender to my inner golden Buddha. Only this pure light is able to forgive and to connect me to all that is. By this time the fire was down to its glow. A gentle melody of gratitude found its way to the lake, which reflected the beautiful colours of the sky out to the first star.

~ Marianne Comtesse

Love is all there is

To experience true love we must be willing to experience anything unlike love, which hides beneath the surface of love. To be torn apart a thousand times over and over again, in the total faith and knowingness that love is all there is. Kahlil Gibran's classic poem from *The Prophet* summarises intimate love. Here is an extract:

When love beckons to you, follow him,
Though his ways are hard and steep.
And when his wings enfold you, yield to him,
Though the sword hidden among his pinions may wound you.
And when he speaks to you, believe in him,
Though his voice may shatter your dreams
as the north wind lays waste the garden.

The way home is always through love. Love is always available. Love as energy is free flowing and does not need attachment. Love your destiny, give it all your passion and wisdom so it can guide you to all the subconscious edges and depths. Don't be fearful, which is the opposite of loving; fear doesn't generate an experience of love. On the contrary live out all feelings and emotions, that appear at the threshold of love's purity to come home again to the Garden of Eden. All roads lead there. It is your choice. *For you are love and it is bigger than you ever imagined. How long and how far can we ride our joy and ecstasy in love?*

Knowing intimacy

Conscious and intimate relationships can be painful, if we do not own our own hurt feelings and projections. And so it is with everyone with whom we create any kind of important relationship.

Your 'mirror' is reflected in your partner and is not to be denied or feared. It will bring you closer to your own truth and growth; there is no escape but to face it. No exits, except back to the heart of love, which is the pillar in any situation. Why ignore it or flee from it? Take it as an invitation to grow and to learn. The key is to let your vulnerability and your ability to surrender to be at play when needed, to let go of any dominance or self-righteousness, to be small and strong at the same time, to let yourself to be seen and heard in all parts you may not like about yourself. Have the courage to show up and let the great mystery unfold.

Allow yourself daily to be acknowledged for who you are and to enhance the sacredness of love.

I used to create war in my relationships, always sensing a lack in my partner, as if he was missing something or not being enough to match me. Conscious of this issue, I was not taking my own projections and unresolved 'stuff' seriously. I did not realise it was all reflected right there in the mirror — my partner. I was never feeling good enough within myself, always striving to be better or smarter, never really settling into that sweet place of surrender of being seen and heard in all my shadows and light. It is human to be innocent. When we are ready to become conscious, life will be revealed in myriad ways.

In the past I went through many layers of abandonment-related issues. In my aloneness I came to realise that separation never exists, as God, the divine love, is forever present. I have come to experience that no matter how big the pains are, there is a higher self within me which guides me through the darkest night of the soul.

Intimacy is a way to experience love up close. For those who don't have an intimate committed relationship, when you meet a new partner or soul companion be gentle and vulnerable and at the same time show your passionate self. Be realistic. Rise in love, don't 'fall in love'! Realise that your partner is your mirror, and is a part of your own personal make-up and story. Your partner is an invitation to grow in devotion. Give space and time to the many hidden projections and tantrum phases on a roller-coaster ride.

Beyond our blindness is the sweetness of intimate love. The mirror is the relationship itself, the reflection of truth. Are we in a fight or are we in a state of peace and trust? There is only someone to fight as long as there is an 'opponent' within you. It is not about avoiding a tantrum or a fight in your relationship, but a question of how quickly can we realise the projection and pull the energy back to take ownership and responsibility for our part in creating the 'war-zone'. *You cannot change your partner, but you can change yourself.* When you take this statement seriously and take conscious and responsible steps to have a better and more truthful relationship with yourself and your partner, life starts to fall into place. You start to sense what a truly divine connection is, an extended experience of embodying God in everything. *As you change, so will your partner, if your relationship is dedicated to emotional and spiritual growth.*

How much are you willing to devote to your 'God-Self', to let go and to clear the things that attach you to the past and unhealthy living?

Entering a committed relationship is when transformations and shifts really can happen. Without commitment you are still doubting, pretending, hiding and fighting your true essence. Commitment is a contract with yourself. It is a responsibility to grow and not run away when it gets too difficult. When intimate relationship becomes a meeting of soul recognition in complete embrace of the light and shadows of each individual, we truly embrace the heart of life that we share. This is the love and union we share with the world and humanity, a force of fullness, truth and magic.

Loving thyself first

In the following practice honour the most important person in the universe, *your self*. Love always starts by loving thyself. How far you go in your self-love will be a direct and clear blueprint of how generously and beautifully you are able to love your fellow beings, as everyone you meet deserves your loving attention.

» Have pen and paper ready to this exercise. Start celebrating self-love by asking: 'What is it sincerely that I love about myself? In which way can I show it to myself?' Write it down in your journal, then state it aloud as you proclaim it.

» Now make a list of what nurtures you, as well as a list of what you celebrate as your accomplishments.

» Give time and space to simply practise one of the activities from your nurturing list in this present moment.

» Start a meditation utilising sound and silence: Visualise being showered with rose petals for all of your accomplishments, as well as for the many ways you have known love, celebrated being nurtured, honoured and accepted. Give sounds to this process and feel the feeling intensify as you continue.

» When you have completed the sounding process, meditate in silence to deepen the beingness and insights, that wish to be revealed to you.

» Journal insights and take a walk to integrate the experience. *Enjoy!*

I gaze into my husband's eyes with the same wonder I would gaze into a baby's eyes, innocently united. I gaze without an agenda, simply letting everything beyond my personality surface, in whatever way I am able to hear, see and perceive this divine presence. I travel alone for long periods of time; though we are committed to the love we share and to love itself. Intense longing may arise when we are apart, but it never comes in the way of the true love. We know it is always there, no matter the physical distance.

An extract about self-love from the movie, *Eat Pray Love*:

Open your heart to love and everything shall follow. For love will never take ownership.

If you are brave enough to leave anything behind you that is familiar and comforting and set out on a true seeking journey either externally or internally, and if you are truly willing to regard anything that happens to you on that journey as a clue, and if you accept anyone you meet along the way as your teacher; and most of all if you are prepared to face and forgive some very difficult realities about yourself, then truth will not be withheld from you.

'Out beyond ideas of wrongdoing
and rightdoing,
there is a field.
I'll meet you there.'

~ Rumi

I stand on a hillside honouring the sunset, allowing its magical colour combinations to infuse me and nurture me. I start to let my voice be heard in tones and lyrics that spontaneously arise. I am ignited with gratitude, my voice is free to express love! I listen, as I hear the echo of the resonance of my voice coming back to me from the valley. I am heard by spirit. A few minutes later a warm shower is warming my body before I am to receive a luxurious massage from loving caring hands. To love myself is to nurture and stimulate what I know gives me great joy and pleasure. To love myself is to be inspired by friends who care. To love myself is to surrender to love others and to be loved. To love myself is to live in an absolute knowingness, that I am love.

CHAPTER 5

Communication with soul

Your resonance and tone of voice
signify the expression of soul
magnified and revealed
and are often more important
than what is communicated.
Your tone and resonance of voice
are an accurate blueprint
of your personality,
your state of being
and soul essence.

During my practitioner training I was preparing for a session with a friend who I knew had some childhood trauma. I didn't know if that issue would arise, and if it did, I didn't know if I could handle it. I knew she had touched on the experience in sessions with others, yet had not fully surrendered. Well, this wonderful woman did in fact go very deep and began releasing great trauma. I wanted to cry because of her pain; I wanted to run because it was so loud and frightening. I didn't know how, with my fear and grief and nervousness, I could keep control of the situation and help her. I focused on her to sense what she needed. I focused on allowing her sounds to fill the room rather than resisting them so I had to put my hands on her; I had to give her some words. I felt the tone, the colour of my voice come from my heart. My heart felt more deep, full, and expansive than ever before. It was the tone, not just the words, not just the sounds, that held me in place and that enveloped her, allowing us both to continue. Soon I needed to meet her more aggressively, and my tone changed. It came from a deep gut feeling of digging my heels in and for both of us to 'get the job done'. And that we did. Her sounds and her emotions escalated until a final release, then calm, then peace. She rested for a long time, her face that of an innocent child. I was full of awe. And, in gratitude for my new discovery: an acute awareness of tone.

This experience more or less forced me to be absolutely in the moment and completely all there. My sounds, words, intentions all came from that place, but the tone revealed even more delicacies of the soul, and took the other soul by the hand. The subtlety of tone is like a work of art. It carries such nuance and feels like gossamer. The elusiveness of how powerfully it can affect our emotions and the core of our being is astounding.   ~ **Lori Lewis**

Sound pioneer and researcher Elizabeth Keyes says in her ground-breaking book *Toning*:

> By the manner in which we speak, every hour of our lives, we set the patterns for our lives. When we realize the vastness of this power, we can appreciate the admonition in the Bible that we shall be held accountable for our every word. At least the tone in which it is spoken!

Imagine a presenter who is enthusiastic with their voice, speaks from a place of embodied emotions, totally alive and playful, fully

present in their being. This is obviously the kind of person who will reach the audience, move us to tears and laughter, give birth to creative ideas and inspiration. This is the kind of person who walks their talk.

In a concert we are moved by singers who dare to touch us deeply emotionally, because they are able to share their life experiences and personality through their vocal expression. They may not be formally trained in skillful singing techniques, but they give themselves fully in their authentic expressions. They are *real* and they are healing us.

The tone of voice reveals

A conscious voice is full of intention. It has a quality which determines how well it is received. Resonance relates to a person's embodiment of their voice, the ability to become all they can be in the present moment, with breath, physicality, emotion, intuition, consciousness, heart and soul.

By changing your tone of voice you change your emotional state of being from within. Believe in the changes you want to make. Let your voice guide you and be heard from your soul and heart.

In important conversations I will often first listen to the tone of the voice, before I focus on what the person is actually speaking about. I may miss some of the linear understanding, but I will be so much better geared to respond, because I have already tuned in to the speaker energetically and emotionally. In fact, if the tone of voice doesn't appeal to me, I will miss most of it anyhow. So be it!

The tone of the voice reveals what's hidden emotionally in the linear, spoken words. Understanding how to fine-tune and use our instrument effectively shifts not only our own consciousness, but also the consciousness of those who receive and hear us. The quality of the voice is what matters to get the intended message across.

➡ **TRY THIS:** Listen to people's voices around you and you may be surprised how much you actually are able to intuit where they are at:

» Listen to a child's voice and sense what you are able to pick up.
» Listen to a close friend's voice, when excited and passionate about what they are communicating.
» Listen to the tone of voice of anyone you meet casually during the day.
» Listen to your own voice's tonality in various situations and notice how the significant vibrations you send out reflect your state of being in the moment.
» Now, play with consciously changing your tone of voice, monitoring what you wish the outcome to be. Take note of the results and adapt your voice for different effects.

Take a moment to look at the subconscious issues you may hide in your voice; look at how often you compare your voice with others. You may be familiar with some of the following self-judgmental statements. Just note it for now, and move on.

» I don't like the way I speak or sound.
» I hope nobody can hear me anyhow.
» I hate my voice.
» I am afraid of being too loud.
» I can't express what I want.
» I am not allowed to be me and tell the truth.
» My voice is not on the right pitch.
» I can't hear myself.
» I can't sing.

Trust judgments; it is human to judge. Do not hold on to judgment, it is a huge drain of energy and life-force. If we have unresolved feelings about somebody, it will immediately affect us and we may eventually start to project unconsciously as an outlet. By becoming conscious with our wording we may start to correct ourselves and transform whatever is holding us in negative patterns. It is a step-by-step process, so be patient.

If we do not know the darkness, how will we ever be able to see and experience the true light? Start to love your voice exactly as it is, thus creating the foundation for it to change.

Our self-talk is powerful and sculpts our subconscious mind. The power of our words is a true shape-shifter. I recently made an exercise of praising a bouquet of flowers several times a day with my sounds, at the same time ignoring a similar bouquet of flowers, giving it only water. The result was staggering. The praised flowers lasted ten days longer!

Core listening in communication

Did you ever have the experience of listening without interruption in a conversation? Often in conversation we impose our ability to judge or advise before the other person has actually shared their story or information. We are often in the fast lane, busy running away from being connected and grounded. We do not allow breaks in our conversation, or space to pause between sentences.

Words may lie, but the tone reflects the true voice. Whether it is expressed or suppressed, our voice is a signature of our soul print.

Our self-righteousness or ego enter conversations within seconds, and our sense of boosting ourselves or knowing better then takes over. I recommend you listen deeply in your next conversation with your child, partner, colleague or friend. Listen without interruption. What does that mean in a dialogue? Listen in such a way that your entire body becomes a listening ear. Then silence will occur. There may even be space between the sentences. Experience a silence within *you* as a listener as well as within the sharing person.

I ask myself, where have we gone if we cannot listen with compassion and give space to one another's soul-felt voice? Where have we gone when we do not give space for silence in conversation?

When you start to become more silent within, you will be able to dwell in a place of inner peace, a healing place. You may even touch a place of freedom, as if all the information has a reference to you and which may then have a vibrational response in your body. A sweet place of *surrender and relaxation*. Maybe a sense of being able to intuit where the other person is at.

Most likely the person you have been listening to in this extraordinary way will feel they are really being heard. By your stepping back and listening with love and compassion they will sense the freedom to express themselves. Not only will you enhance your own communication skills with this practice, but the person who is being listened to will start to make greater progress in true communication.

The following practice is an effective step to come to the core of what listening in conversation actually means. When I give a similar exercise in the Soul Voice introductory workshop I often hear: '*I feel I am being heard for the first time in my life!*'

Soul resonance and soul attraction

What we send out to the universe, comes back to us. We send out a vibration, a message, and the universe acts as a magnet for it to be picked up and returned in like manner.

When we are in our heart and soul it is very difficult to be superficial or false at any level — physical, emotional, spiritual or mental. If you only desire life on a physical level, you only resonate on a physical  level, which is a small part of the whole. The more conscious we become of the resonance we project in any given moment, the more we act as a magnet for what we actually need on a soul level.

To live life in resonance with our soul purpose means that we create a way of living and of being that enables us to be in harmony with our surroundings. We take responsibility for staying grounded in these fast-moving times, and we are able to respond accordingly to our optimal growth and development.

When I make a presentation to an audience or facilitate a seminar I rejoice in stretching my voice to the fullest spectrum of its resonant capacity, which allows the audience to listen deeper. I visualise my voice being an instrument of both low and high frequencies. I undulate my voice to encompass a wider spectrum of emotions, so that I am able to pick up on the audience's receptivity. I incorporate speaking consciously from both my upper as well as lower body, which allows me to stay grounded using both my yin and my yang voice: its vulnerability and sensitivity as well as its strength and power. I modulate my tone of voice as I emphasise to the audience to expect an unpredictable journey of information, that is meant to touch the heart and awaken the soul.

I love to surprise myself by making sounds in the midst of my speech. I may pick up on energy from sceptical persons and sound intentionally to their subconscious. By doing intuitive sounding in my presentation the audience is better able to be in an open, intuitive space. They not only come more in resonance with their own vibration, but also with the group energy as a whole. The results are often remarkable. After the presentation I ask the

EXERCISE

Listening with soul

Listening intently to the tone of voice of a person speaking is an exercise in slowing down communication. This exercise will strengthen your ability to listen. It can give profound reflections for both partners involved about what listening and communicating with soul actually means. **Note:** this challenging exercise is to be done with a partner.

» Sit in front of each other and eye-gaze for a moment, one to two metres apart. Let your eyes relax, and breathe consciously. Decide which role each will play in the first round: who is first to share and who is the listener?

» The person who speaks starts to communicate from the heart.

» For the listener: relax into your body by listening to your breath for a moment. Listen so that your entire being becomes a listening ear; thus you will most likely have a sensation of dropping in and falling down. Let yourself be filled with love and compassion for the speaking person.

» If at any time you want to say something, hold back; sink into your body as you let go any sensation of being in your head and choose to dwell in the body. Be still and empty. If you feel an urge to say anything, simply let go or consciously compost the energy into the earth.

» When the sharing is complete, take a moment of silence to reflect. The listening person: What did you observe and pick up in the tone of voice? Did you perceive any colours or images? What was the speaking person in contact with or not aware of? How did you receive what was shared and communicated? What did you learn about yourself in this process? Did you find it hard to keep yourself quiet without commenting?

» The speaker: What did you get across that made a difference? What did you observe within yourself as you were heard and not interrupted? Did you find answers to some of your questions?

» Share your insights and experiences with one another.

» When the sharing is complete, journal the experience before reversing roles. *Enjoy!*

audience to practise a couple of sound-exercises; the letting-go process and trusting the intuitive response have already been established. I am able to get across what I really wish to convey in a stronger, contained energy.

Where attention goes, energy flows.

To reach the heart and the soul of others we need our non-linear brain to be activated in our speech. I encourage you to dare to be different to wake up humanity and allow your intentions to be manifested by simply speaking dynamically, creatively and with all your passion. Make an effort to become conscious of your tone of voice, especially in endeavours that really matter to you. Be creative about what you wish to get across by playing on all the strings of your instrument, your voice.

Transform your surroundings

Sounding with heart and soul can be easy when we stay away from labelling or analysing — simply make a sound and then another. Continue for a couple of minutes and suddenly a new reality is born out of the most simple form of using the voice. It's magic. Remember, playing with sounds revitalises and rejuvenates our cells and bones. Get your daily boost from sounding: it doesn't cost anything and there is very little effort involved.

➡ TRY THIS:

» Sound and sing in the shower.

» Sound while doing gardening, cooking meals, washing the dishes, cleaning the house, taking a walk, sending emails, driving the car, doing the laundry.

» Sing and sound with your children. They love to play and experience who they are when making sounds.

» Give your relationship a boost by doing sound exercises together. This may open up to more spontaneous sounds during lovemaking.

» Sound during your breaks at work; it works no matter what your job is.

» Lighten up your colleagues by daring to express and be courageous!

» Make sounds together with your pets: listen to them, imitate them and respond to them.

» In your garden, in the forest or at the beach, sound intuitively. Vocalise your feelings to the trees, the ocean, the birds, the flowers, the earth.

» If you come into a room where the atmosphere feels out of balance, take the courage to use your voice and tune into the vibration needed to make a transformation.

Imagine all gatherings and meetings on Planet Earth starting with giving sounds to the heart and from the heart of the gathering. What a symphony and 'wow'! What a transformation we could experience overnight.

» If you are in a conversation where the energy between the two of you is unclear, make the sound needed to immediately change the energy.
» If you feel helpless before an important rendezvous or appointment, play with your tone of voice to instantly change your mood.

Your voice is your wisdom keeper. Let it remember as it remembers YOU.

A student told me in an email that since the last assignment I gave her on 'igniting intuitive sounding from the heart', she had almost not been able to stop sounding and singing throughout the entire day. What a joy to be connected to soul in this magical yet simple way! What a joy to be understood through the pure vibration of voice.

EXERCISE
Sound to the soul of humanity

This is an advanced exercise, so proceed only when you are ready. You will send your energy in sound vibration and intention to your loved ones and to humanity. You will open yourself to a greater heart-connection within and will experience abundance as you come to realise that receiving is giving and giving is receiving.

» Sit in a comfortable position and tune into a meditative state by breathing deeply and letting go of any unwanted thoughts. Relax into listening to your body-wisdom.

» Listen to any soul-felt communication you have had recently, and let it dwell in your heart with hopeful appreciation.

» Now activate the soul essence from your heart by making sound frequencies that fill the room. Let the sound spread with waves of strengthening intensity and intention. Dwell for a time in that presence. Bring forth your intuitive sounding.

» When ready, visualise your family, your loved ones and your community receiving your soul-felt sounds through the ether. Simply think about those you are directing your energy to, and consciously send them your heartfelt energy and compassion. Trust that your sounds and clear intention will reach them. Trust that whatever you sound will carry through.

» Allow the energy to come back to you by simply receiving instead of giving. Rest in silence for a while and receive the integration of the energy you sent out, be it through colours, images, feelings or insights. Stay open to the experience.

» When ready, finish and stand up. Make sounds which connect you to earth and ground you. Stay in gratitude.

» Journal or draw the experience. *Enjoy!*

Being completely present in the moment, without attachment,
allows you to transcend the mundane daily routine.
You become vibrantly alive as you realise you are not
separated from Source.
You communicate as a channel between heaven and earth
as you embody your soul's destiny with faith and trust.
Dwell in meditative presence; express your soul.
Simply focus your intention on what you desire and
let your voice bring it into manifestation and fruition
without attachment to the outcome.
Give eternal thanks for the voice the Creator gave you.
Let it soar and be heard.

CHAPTER 6

The inner child's spontaneity

*The inner child knows us
before we know it.
Invite it in to taste
the ecstasy of life,
to soar with the wings of play and magic.
Let's start all over again and
stay in the beginning,
being an innocent child.*

Monkey attraction! Since I was a child I loved to play with monkey toys or to watch movies with monkeys living freely in the jungle. Why? In my shyness I was observing the outer world, as a prisoner in my inner world. For so many years I was sad not to be able to express my playfulness and wild nature. I didn't allow myself to be!

The Soul Voice journey gave me the 'right kick' to plunge into liberation of this little monkey in a cage, to give her a voice to be expressed, to be heard and to be loved. I learned not to be perfect, to be patient with myself and I discovered a multi-talented being, me! I never was so creative, so close to my emotions, so willing to live it out, to fully express myself and my true nature. By diving into the depth of the darkness, guided by the power of my unique voice, I could access this precious treasure within me.

The little monkey did grow and now owns her own power, ready to realise her dreams. Every day I nourish this wise part of my being in trust and in faith, having fun, knowing that I'm well guided by my intuition and my instinct. I feel deep gratitude and infinite joy to finally have found the core essence of myself, my courageous enthusiastic inner child!   ~ **Amira Pacentra**

We came into this world as very sensitive beings. As children we had phenomenal intuition, a magnificent imagination and a spontaneity able to show all emotions. We could hear and see beyond the ordinary, and express freely in the moment. We basked on the wings of freedom in a place of timelessness where play was our reality and our guide.

As we became adults we lost contact with our inner child's imagination, creativity and magic. Efficiency, productivity and expectations from society took over and adrenalin kicked in to get things done quickly. Ignoring our inner voice, we tried to fit into society's structure and limited, limiting beliefs. We lost contact at the expense of innocence, purity and real play.

What we have lost can only come back to us in higher forms, when we work consciously with that loss. It is never too late to regain this precious contact and bring your inner child alive again. The children around us are constant reminders to do so!

It is said that 'except that you become like a child again, you cannot enter the Kingdom of God.' Without reclaiming our

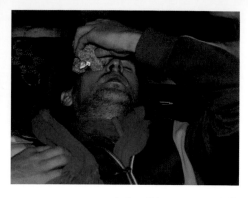

innocence and the wonder of life, we are lost.

Researcher of inner child work, Dr Newton Kondaveti explains:

We are all inherently magnificent beings with limitless potential for experiencing and expressing unconditional love, joy and creativity. However, to fully experience our true nature, the child within must be embraced and expressed. Unless we reconnect with our inner child in a safe and unconditional environment, the child within will remain isolated and alone. Unless we reclaim our childlike feelings like sensitivity, wonderment and aliveness, our inner child will remain wounded. By regaining our childlike qualities of spontaneity, creativity and playfulness, we will be able to live with unconditional love and joy. By fully reintegrating with our inner child, we can become complete human beings and once again feel whole.

Who is the inner child?

The inner child is a potent and precious energy that originates in our childhood memories and experiences. It resides in the core of our being, and since childhood it has developed to become a part of our adult self, either expressed, suppressed or forgotten. The inner child has a voice that is sensitive, vulnerable and honest, a voice that knows, no matter how much we may have ignored it or what kind of childhood we may have had. Maybe your inner child's voice is so quiet that you need silent moments to be able to hear it. Maybe the inner child is covered by all kinds of emotions, false ideas, images or expectations. Maybe it is just out of sight, waiting to be named, called in and noticed.

Take a deep breath now and trust it is there somewhere. Let your inner child become active through play and inner listening. We become so serious when we forget our precious inner child. Really serious! Too much seriousness just boosts our ego but does not make us happy. Taking care of life's daily obligations, paying bills, keeping appointments, doing what's necessary to survive should not compromise our time out with our playful inner child.

How do we stop being a slave to our habits and our usual way of thinking and doing? How do we wake up and take a break from being preoccupied with achieving, doing and communicating? In this moment, as you read on, get a renewed perspective on your life through the way your inner child speaks to you. Do not bother about the outcome — it will be apparent when you take the actions needed. You are not a lost child, you are a magical child!

There is no way I can get a new group of people to sound the most unfamiliar and provocative sounds without engaging their inner child's innocence and playfulness. There is no way to fully open up to freedom without letting the inner child be active; as we do so we will move mountains. There is no way I am able to get people to let go of stubborn control and judgmental ideas about how they sound or how they should sound, without letting the inner child rule.

The inner child is an expression of our most authentic and vulnerable yet creative self. It is a personality, a significant being who lives within us, and most often has been ignored as we have grown up. It has become a civilised adult and put in a box; it has covered up its innate spontaneity and joy. Do you remember the magic you experienced as a child living in a natural state of free expression, fully engaged? What we saw and experienced was real; imagination became reality. Time seemed to stop. In touch with

'Life is not complicated for a child.
It lives fully in the present moment,
enjoying what it is doing.
It does not really worry about tomorrow
and what it may bring.
Life is good for that child . . .
Life is fun,
life is glorious and exciting,
that is really living as you should live.'
~ EILEEN CADDY, FOUNDER OF
THE FINDHORN FOUNDATION

our emotions, we would tell the world what's going on through outbursts of crying, screaming, wailing, laughing, singing, and with no worries about how we sounded.

A child is pure and present and rarely untruthful or boring to play with, right? Their body language and their tone of voice will quickly indicate where they are at, so even if they are trapped or unhappy they know this is not a natural state of being. *Children know that deep inside they are the light of the world, and that it's natural to have fun, to be playful and happy.* What a gift!

Staying innocent and curious

Look into a child's eyes and receive true wonder and mystery. The purity and innocence of children is contagious and seductive. I repeat: *Without becoming like a child over and over again, we cannot enter the kingdom of heaven.* This was how we came into this world and this is hopefully how we will leave this world, innocent as a child, but more wise.

The inner child is the spark of life, the juice and the elixir that make life worth living. No matter how terrible our childhood memories may have been, or how many hurt feelings we carry in our cellular body, the inner child is still there whispering in our ears to come out and play, to nurture the inner magic.

Children operate from their subconscious 50% of the time, while we adults are using only 10–15%. It's from our subconscious reservoir that our imagination and dreamtime originate; it's in the subconscious that we store our hidden potential and our deep inner knowingness, as well as our shadow sides. We long for this exquisite curiosity and innocence to unfold; to wake up to a new day with the eyes of a child in wonder and with unlimited possibilities.

> Like a child who is just taking its first step with a loving parent who knows this child will one day run with the wind, God sees in us our unlimited potential — fulfilled. It is only us who ever see limits or apparent lack in our life.   — **Chip Richards**

One of the great qualities the inner child frees within us is laughter. If you observe conversations with lots of laughter, it is a sign of the inner child being activated, although too much laughter can also be an escape from reality. The inner child's laughter is liberating and such a great healer; the more we laugh, the easier life becomes, and in addition, it is stretching the heart muscles! Don't try to stop laughing, if you have started a laugh almost impossible to stop! Here is a journal entry from one such experience:

> *That ignition of laughter, just can't stop it, although the abdomen muscles have signalled 'stop' long ago. I feel infinite and without boundaries, it is an ecstatic state I want to remain in, maybe without the expression of laughter! I perceive figures, shapes, colours, sounds, movements that I normally do not perceive in daily life. I realise by staring at a tiny grass straw that we are all light beings and light is all there is. My hands are hot and my heart is beating with a very soothing pulse, slightly accelerated. I start to move my body in a slow motion walk. The next thing I notice is my voice transforms from laughter to singing ancient tones — a calling, a haunting almost. It reminds me of the sound of the earth, how the earth would sound, when we start to listen to its vibration in the midst of a*

wild unspoiled nature. I can barely keep my eyes opened any longer, and I allow them to close. My singing transforms into humming and the humming won't stop. My heart is humble and my soul remembers. I am in my body — I am in the human flesh. My voice and my inner child are connected and I now know, we were never separated.

In the past the inner child felt hurt and scared, burdened with shyness and hidden abandonment issues, memories of not being taken care of and being judged for not doing the right things. It was when I started to honour my feelings and take myself really seriously that I discovered Her. I had moments saying *I cannot live without you*, but without knowing at that time who I was talking to.

As I went deeper into working with all the forbidden and scary emotions, including my inadequacies, my voice became significantly reborn. I could forgive those who had hurt me and those who didn't understand me when I was rebelliously demonstrating my rights.

I now know that the inner child is closer to me than my own heartbeat. She is always real and present; She is there to love and support me in all circumstances. She is there to remind me that life is playful and always creative. She is also the voice who tells me, *I will never leave you*, as She emanates a strong commitment and protection. If I come into a situation I want to run away from, hide in fear, play numb or 'dead', I call upon Her and She hears me instantly and whispers, *I love you and you are safe.*

Allow your inner child's spontaneity to be expressed any time you have the chance, or simply take the chance. *Do what surprises you, do what for you is unpredictable or unknown. The inner child loves surprises!*

➡ TRY THIS:

» Cuddle a teddy bear; remind yourself what it feels like to be a child.

» Take some drawing paper and coloured pencils and start to draw the inner child.

» Do an activity unfamiliar to you — maybe it is risky, scary or even forbidden. Ask your inner child if it wants to go roller skating, jump on a trampoline, draw in the sand, ride a bicycle or fly a paper dart?

» Tell your child positive affirmations as you celebrate and embrace its innocence.

» Watch a sunset that leaves you in awe as you reawaken your inner child's eyes to mystery. Or watch the billions of stars on a clear night. It truly is mystery, and only if you can feel this deep within your heart will your inner child wake, and you will know what I am talking about.

Your inner child's world may be simple. In fact we often need to come back to basics and simplicity to understand how the inner child can cope with adult consciousness and become *our guide*. Let everything matter: how you walk, the way you drink your tea, coffee or juice, the way you do your morning ritual in the bathroom. Let these new eyes and ears be filled with mystery and spontaneity as you allow your inner child to be in charge throughout the day.

Make a commitment to yourself that you will never ignore your inner child again. Be compassionate, loving and patient when you go through difficult times with yourself and then call Her or Him forward. Do not resist the inner child, but invite the challenge. When you have opened the jewel box of the inner child, joy becomes an expression of freedom in daily life.

Go only as far as you feel safe in these discoveries, and seek professional help if you need to.

Your inner child wants to be spontaneous and playful; it wants to have fun and be real. DO YOU?

I decided to spent a full day with myself at the zoo, a place that can easily stimulate my inner child and joyful excitement. I love being with the animals, being so close to them, smelling them, observing them, connecting and communicating with them.

At a certain moment I suddenly felt abandoned: I realised that I was at the zoo all by myself and I felt so lonely and isolated. So I just sat there for a while with the birds, just being, and then the feeling subsided. Luckily, the magical inner child was most present. I saw everything through her eyes, with sheer excitement; it was like experiencing all the animals for the first time. I was so happy and excited, all the colours were brighter, all the sounds I listened to and expressed myself were much more nuanced than usual, all the odours from the animals were very present as well.

I experienced that when I truly am present with the animals, not just passing by and looking at them, but truly connecting intensely, they feel it and they are more than willing to connect and share with me. I just have to receive, listen and let my intuition receive all their wisdom and messages. I had eye contact with many animals and it touched something so deep in me that I felt happy

Have fun in gibberish

This exercise awakens the inner child. It is also a great exercise for taking yourself less seriously. It relaxes the left brain, and can be used successfully even during an argument.

» Start with some syllables which do not make sense to you; for example, *di di di yoo yoo yoo ka ka ka ma ma ma, hu hu hu ta ta*. Then weave them together ... *dima huta yooyoo kamahuta* ... then let it take off ... *kubi tasa fani bila humakatu rasidi ah hola* ... etc.

» Have fun as you play with any syllables. Be spontaneous and do not think about what you are doing. You are birthing your unique gibberish language! These sounds originate from a part of the brain we used as a child, before linear language.

» Now imagine you have an intention for the so-called 'gibberish'; you can express 'happiness' in this language for example, or you can 'gibberish' how it is to read this book, or how you felt in an recent argument. Any subject can be transformed through this language.

» When you are finished, draw or journal the experience to integrate it. Note any underlying emotions that have been processed. *Enjoy!*

and humble. There is so much to learn from our animal friends. And truly, it was amazing communicating with the animals for a whole day! An unforgettable experience just sitting there with the butterflies, the giraffes, the bears, the seals and many other animal friends and just eye-gazing with them, communicating without words but in body language and heart, and now and then with sounds.

~ Lill-Ann Berger

How to ignite further the contact with the inner child

It is not always possible to be in magical contact with the inner child; this precious being may also be rebellious and unpredictable, demonstrating awkward behaviours. It has many 'sub-personalities', some of which may carry lifelong hurt feelings

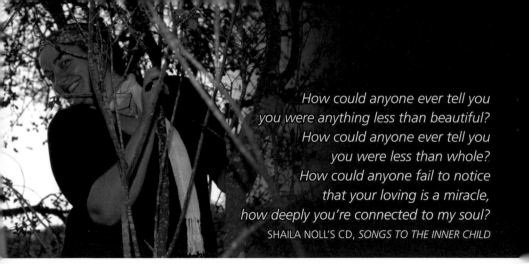

or may be afraid of being seen and intimate. Our inner child also relates to how we have been dealing with our mother and father issues. As this is a ongoing process for most people, this is not where we start in this moment. As an immediate approach we will begin with an easy access to your inner child's world. Don't give up, be persistent. it is waiting for you to knock on the door, so take this invitation and opportunity seriously. You may think, *Oh yes, I am already in contact with my inner child*, that's great! Do something purposeful about it then, and make a commitment to have your inner child as a more permanent guide.

EXERCISE
The mirror to find YOU

Practise this challenging exercise when you are ready. It allows you to start to remember and recognise your inner child and what it wishes to communicate.

» Find a hand mirror or a mirror on the wall, sit in front of it and eye-gaze with yourself. Take a few deep breaths and feel centred in your heart. This exercise may take five to ten minutes. The mirror doesn't lie; it sees and knows you. Trust what you perceive and do not judge. Become aware of freeing yourself from preoccupying thoughts by connecting with your breath. Listen to the inner self and, if you discover you wish to be somebody other than the person you actually see, let that go.

» Now focus on seeing the inner child in your whole expression. She or he may be most apparent in your eyes, cheeks and around your mouth. Or you may be able to capture an overall impression by staring at yourself intently. Remember to breathe. Look for innocence, openness, humour and play; listen with trust for the inner child's voice.

» Continue the intense focus and believe in this inner child, regardless of what you perceive. Let colours, images or memories come to the surface and reveal themselves.

» Talk to your inner child, aloud or silently. Let the contact you have expand as you become better acquainted with her or him.

» Each time you do this exercise, new treasures will be revealed to you.

» When you feel complete, stop eye-gazing and leave the mirror. Lie down on the floor and relax for a while. Draw or journal the experience when you are ready and be thankful for this unique experience. *Enjoy!*

*I once was lost
but now I am found.
I will never leave you
alone again.
I love you and
I treasure you.
I am always right here with you.*

CHAPTER 7

Freeing expression
through 'therapeutic acting'

Ride the waves of fear and express those fears.
This is a process of owning your own reality,
from which point you can do anything.
There is nothing you cannot handle
when you love yourself and your expression fully
in 'therapeutic acting'.
You may discover
that your only safety net is God within.
Your magical inner voice will guide you.

My experience of 'therapeutic acting' was profound and a huge leap in my journey of self-development. We had four hours to create a presentation to portray 'our story' through authentic acting. We were a group of four working both individually and together, and were two and a half hours into practising our presentation when Karina came along to see how we were doing. This happened to be as I was acting out my story. Within a few minutes of watching what I was doing, she stopped me and told us that we would have to start all over again. Her words were 'I was not being authentic, not 'feeling' my story' … and left us to it to come up with the truth!

I was so angry … how dare she do that to me, to us, when we had worked for so long and so hard on our presentation? I wanted to run away. But there was nowhere to run. I would be taking me with me wherever I went. If I ran away from this, would I always run when things became too difficult?

My mind was blank. My anger was not allowing my brain to function in order for creativity to flow. The others in my group were in the same boat, but one of our group members brought us back into focus. With less than an hour, we put our presentation together. And unfold it did!

We started with my story, which originated from a very traumatic time in my life. I fell into the 'acting trap' but then off I went! I was no longer acting, I was real, I was living the now fully as never before. From there, the whole performance was totally authentic; there was no need to pretend, as the truth is all there is. I felt so liberated, I totally let go and I was me. How wonderful, how exhilarating, how exciting! Tears, pain, laughter, joy, dance, euphoria — everything was there. By halting my pretence that day, I received a special gift. I am truly grateful.   ~ **Pene Mckay**

Acting is holistic when the soul of the actor gets to the core — not as a role they play to embody somebody else, but by being their absolute, ultimate self. When standing in front of an audience you are asked to dive deeper into your absolute authenticity, to be 100% in the here and now with all the fears and emotions that may make your heart beat faster and faster!

Our physical and psychological conditions are reflected in the vitality of our vocalisations. Each student is so different and unique; I learn so much from each and every one when they show up and commit themselves to the work. The way we express ourselves in life is a direct imprint of our inner world and psyche, which contain a rich reservoir of characters, sub-personalities, images, moods and memories. We are indeed composed of many different personalities, a complete mystery and tapestry of multi-dimensional voices and masks, which we oftentimes only access through dreams or deep therapeutic healing work.

Gabrielle Roth, founder of 'The Five Rhythms' says:

> The art of sacred living means being a holy actor, acting from the soul rather than the ego. The soul is out of space and time and hence always available, an ever-present potential of our being. It is up to each of us to celebrate and to actualize our being, and to turn each meal, conversation, outfit, letter, and so on, into art. Every mundane activity is an opportunity for full, authentic self-expression. The soul is our artistic self, our capacity for transforming every dimension of our lives into art and theater.

My personal vocation into holistic acting

Since childhood, acting has been thrilling excitement. As a teenager I played significant roles and dived right into them. Acting brought me out of my self-indulgent seriousness and my 'brainwashed tendencies'. It gave me hope that maybe there was something out there awaiting me beyond the mundane trivial world. No surprise that I chose acting as a career. I enrolled at a body, mime and mask theatre in Paris. Was there any future

in this, my parents asked me? They doubted, but I didn't. I was lucky to be accepted as a 19-year-old at Lecoq's International Mime and Mask School; everyone else was 21. My experience at Lecoq brought me to the realisation that *we are not just all things but we are the embodiment of all things*. The child's dream realised with a conscious adult's mind and body was a huge spiritual awakening and a rough ride. Every day my face was covered entirely with a neutral mask to go through very intense identification processes. We were taught how to embody any imaginable 'living thing': an element, an animal, an emotion, a colour, an object, a persona, a demon, anything — and in movement only, no speech! The improvisations didn't stop. Lots of competition; lots of heartbreaking transformations. Lots of improvisations working with the unknown where you were pushed to fill the present moment with all you had to give. The next step was learning the identification process with a half-mask on your face, which included sounds and linear language.

Wow, another challenge and a big roller-coaster ride. The mask shadowed our ego and mind-thinking process. The impulses were destined to come from the body's own innate wisdom. Stripping off the layers of illusion and control made us naked. The body was constantly guiding us, not the mind.

This hard work at such an early age brought me to reside in my soul centre, which is also called the chi centre, the main energy vortex in the human body situated a couple of centimetres below the navel. It is our centre of the unknown, the subconscious, dreamtime, creative impulses and grounded manifestation. From here, all movement originates. If you are not in contact with your soul centre, you simply cannot play the role.

The neutral mask shadows our ego and mind-thinking process. The impulses are then destined to come from the body's own innate wisdom.

Years later I launched my own mask theatre company in Denmark, producing a one-woman show playing eight mask-characters, each being part of my inner sub-personalities, as well as reflecting many parts of humanity's subconscious layers. The whole act and touring with this production was an intense process. I prayed often to God, asking to be shown if this was my true destiny, to teach humanity about their unconscious role-playing by being an actress.

A couple of years later I ended up at the Carnival in Venice, a huge highlight in my life at that time. I had no idea what I had signed up for, but my intuition strongly called me to go. Mask-theatre lived out in indescribable dimensions in the streets of this beautiful, ancient city. It was my first time in Venice, and an unbelievable heart-opener to see everyone being performers, interacting with each other as if they truly were the characters they were playing. The walking streets of Venice seemed transformed

into a 'nirvana' vibration, uplifted by the living history of the city's majestic past.

I was walking the streets being *her*, my chosen character. And I got it! I became Her: in this role a part of me was living in another lifetime and at the same time I was myself in this present moment. I recall I went into a transcendental state. I was not only the identity I knew from my one-woman show, but also this past-life figure. I experienced a 'satori state' of being in two parallel universes simultaneously; this other lifetime and my here-and-now reality. I felt no separation whatsoever, only divine presence.

This mystical experience led me many years afterwards to a seminar at the Esalen Institute in California, where Hollywood actress Paula Shaw was teaching an 'Acting to the max' workshop. Meanwhile I had changed career and become a counsellor, bodyworker, rebirther and voice healing therapist. I was so excited about what happened in this seminar, I barely slept for three nights. Paula combined acting and therapy in an extraordinary format, spiced with impeccable and inspirational techniques. I felt I already knew what she was teaching somehow, but it was obvious I needed to go through the process and dive deeper into my 'raw skin'.

Dare the ultimate expression

What is life without taking risks? What is life without going to the extremes of what is possible, to discover you can do it? What is life without daring to jump into the unknown without a safety net underneath you? *In this freefalling only your magical inner child and inner voice can guide you.*

I have created a technique called 'Therapeutic acting' or 'Therapeutic self-expression'. It is a compelling and risky stretch of our creative expression. It is like being torn apart a thousand times and being challenged to the

The ultimate expression will set you free.
It is not a question of comparing yourself with others, or avoiding being ridiculous or outrageous.
It is about daring to live.

max. Only by showing our nakedness in all its facets will we truly descend in order to ascend with a pulsing heart beating faster and faster, the more we try to perform instead of just being who we are!

When we stand 'naked' in front of a group of people, without any defences, restrictions or preconceptions, anything which is fearful or not owned will start to act out or shake, searching for an outlet.

We are composed of many sub-personalities, each of which has a distinct voice and expression, which longs to be shown and expressed fully.

When we are not bothered about the outcome or preoccupied with being ridiculed, we will start to live for real! The inevitable fear guides us to become either real or fake. You will come to experience that *the ultimate expression will set you free.*

Dare!

It is not a question of comparing yourself with others or avoiding being ridiculous or outrageous. Your soul gets ignited in this act of resurrection. Your body is pushed to follow its guidance as you realise there is nothing you cannot handle, or that is too big when you love yourself and your expression fully.

The stage then becomes reality, it becomes life itself, a place where you get awakened from the dream you have always dreamt, to *be* and manifest.

Be nothing and be everything

Be courageous in practising this exercise. Perhaps you have never been more ready than right now. Or you may want to read on and come back to it at another time. It will challenge you — your identity, your ego and your soul.

» Place yourself on the floor in standing position; start to relax deeply into your spine. Let go of thoughts by sounding some *ah*-sounds. Relax and let go. Imagine a circle of friends, relatives and strangers gathered. They have come to see and to hear *you*. Listen to your heartbeat and just be.

» At this point of time you are enough as you are — without doing anything. Radiate your honesty. Only by being completely authentic will you be accepted. Your audience can look right through you, so no faking.

Don't be afraid of being ridiculous or outrageous: your 'naked' presence is radiating what you are thinking, feeling and processing. All your thoughts, energetic movements and emotions being are perceived by the audience around you.

» After ten minutes 'on stage doing nothing' you can relax. Lie down on the floor and sink into your breathing and listening.

» When you are ready, journal or draw the experience to integrate it. Take a walk in nature. *Enjoy!*

I listen to a student on stage, as I watch her movements and uncomfortable expressions. I have asked her to live out '*Who am I?*' Her tone of voice is fragile as words struggle to be expressed freely, hiding in grief. I then guide her through a couple of challenging exercises, asking her to express the hidden grief I hear in her voice by recalling a recent source of her emotion. At the same time she is asked to identify with becoming the ocean in her body movements, to support and exaggerate the deep letting-go process. In the next practice I ask her to sound as an emotionally charged opera singer. I emphasise, 'Do not be perfect,' and she takes off. Within minutes all her inadequacies and inhibitions have disappeared. She is fully her authentic, soul-felt self.

Who am I?

Be patient and practise this exercise when it is appropriate — only you will know. Freeing your creative self-expression is a courageous act of surrender and resurrection that uses all your imagination to reach freedom and serenity.

» Stand in front of a mirror where you are able to see most of your body. Observe your face, its contours and expressions. Start to make funny faces and sounds to massage your facial expression. Continue to play, letting go of anything that wants to be expressed.

» Be in contact with your chi centre below the navel. Express the feeling in your body through creative sounding. Go for it wholeheartedly. Forget about yourself and move your body accordingly. Take risks! Use the mirror when you need to. Express what makes you feel uncomfortable. Express what is scary and puts you on the edge. Express an extreme. No hiding, go for it. You are being seen and heard.

» Be somebody; choose a subject or a sub-personality and identify 100% with it. Live it out fully in improvisation, sounds, monologue, body movements and emotional expressions.

» Conclude by coming back once more to gazing intensely into the mirror, without expression. Be neutral and enjoy the silence for a while.

» When you are ready, draw and journal the experience. Go for a walk in nature to further ground the experience if possible. *Enjoy!*

Taking a leap of faith

Your stage can start in your own living room: the stage is the playground to know thyself. When the character you play matches your true calling, you come home. Your authenticity brings you home, which then will become your success. Most of us play many roles during a lifetime, but the most important role is the one which rocks, inspires, ignites, challenges and teaches you the most. And you will certainly make a difference to humanity by living and breathing that role to its fullest potential.

Take that leap of faith, take that chance to dance with your infinite self on whatever 'dance floor' awaits you. Celebrate your uniqueness and let the world be a better place to live because you have made this commitment.

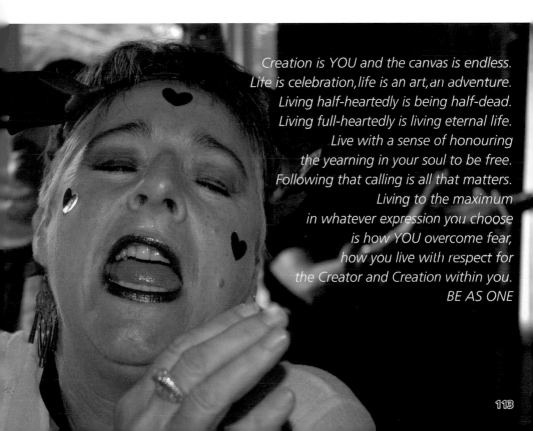

Creation is YOU and the canvas is endless.
Life is celebration, life is an art, an adventure.
Living half-heartedly is being half-dead.
Living full-heartedly is living eternal life.
Live with a sense of honouring
the yearning in your soul to be free.
Following that calling is all that matters.
Living to the maximum
in whatever expression you choose
is how YOU overcome fear,
how you live with respect for
the Creator and Creation within you.
BE AS ONE

CHAPTER 8

Breath, a gateway to voice

'Your hand opens and closes and opens and closes.
If it were always a fist or always stretched open,
you would be paralysed.
Your deepest presence is in every
small contracting and expanding,
the two as beautifully
balanced and coordinated
as bird wings.'
~ Rumi

Breath is the wave on which we speak and sound, the exchange between the inner and the outer world. The way we breathe determines how we feel and sound at any given moment. It is a metaphor for life; it is a motion of falling and rising, ebbing and flowing, receiving and giving, entering and leaving. Every bone, muscle, nerve and cell is awakened by it. Breath is the fundamental ingredient of the human voice; it is the passage of air past the vocal cords that creates sound.

It is from breath awareness that we develop a full and rich voice resonance, a stronger connection to soul and emotions. Breath and voice cannot be separated.

Breath is the vital exchange of oxygen in the lungs which, via the blood, is transported to all the cells of our body. Our heartbeat and our breath rhythm are interconnected. Our heartbeat is dependent on how well we breathe — the heart being the centre of our expression to both the inner and the outer world. Deep, conscious breathing gives a richer and fuller resonance, and thus connects us more strongly to the intention of expression. Look at the indigenous cultures of Africa, where tribal songs and sound medicine are expressed naturally, as a part of a powerful connection between heart and breath.

Jerzy Grotowski, a remarkable theatre researcher and founder of the 'Poor Theater', says:

> Breathing is an organic and spontaneous process. Exercises are not intended to submit it to strict control, but to correct any anomalies whilst retaining its spontaneity.

Breathing without restriction

Breath in Greek mythology means soul. Through breath we are interconnected with all that is. Being spontaneous, being fully engaged in the moment is what we long for. Children are much more skilful at this than adults.

Breath is the foundational source which sustains our vitality. When a child is born there is a very sacred moment of taking its first breath. The cutting of the umbilical cord brings the baby into individuality.

Did you ever notice when holding a baby that every single part of its body moves with its breathing? Let's not forget this as we grow into being an adult.

Frederick Leboyer, a French doctor and scientist, founded 'Birth without Violence' and inspired mothers to give birth as a respectful natural process in peaceful surroundings. 'Lotus Birth' is another example of this new paradigm. In 'lotus birth' the newborn stays with the placenta until the cord detaches from the baby naturally. Breathing for the newborn is not just the breath itself; it also signifies the coming into this world ready to be an individual human being. It is the moment of reconnecting to Source, as the breath connects us not only to the world but also to Spirit.

How do we come back to living fully by embodying the breath?

))) EXERCISE
The full deep breath

By practising this breathing exercise regularly you will imprint into your conscious and subconscious being a new awareness of breath in your daily life. Conscious breathing genuinely affirms and celebrates life. A full deep breath is energising and cleansing. It teaches you to relax and to let life come to you, to live in your body and in cellular aliveness.

» Lie down in a relaxed position and observe the rhythm of your breathing.

» Pay attention to letting your jaw be wide open, and let the breath move freely through you. Start to exaggerate your breathing. Breathe more deeply and watch your body's response to that. Accept whatever you observe. Aim for the inhaling and exhaling breath to be of equal length.

» Take a few breaths and observe your tummy muscles. On the inhaling breath expand your tummy muscles, which gives a sensation of being bigger and fuller. Put your hands on the tummy to feel the movement. You may also notice the pelvic floor moving.

» When you exhale, relax the muscles and let the tummy return to normal. Surrender, and remember to be very slow and gentle.

» The next step is to observe the abdominal muscles (around the ribcage) in the same way as you practised with the tummy muscles.

» When both the tummy and the abdominal muscles are consciously being activated you may add the chest muscles (the heart muscles). This sensation is of uplifting the whole upper body, filling your lungs with air. Exhale and let your lungs deflate. Do this slowly and gently, observing the movement of the chest muscles.

» Finally, combine all muscle groups of the full deep breathing exercise in the order mentioned above. Practise this combination until you can do it smoothly and easily.

» You are now ready to make an *ah*-sound on the exhaling breath, using the full deep breathing awareness described above. Open your mouth wide and make a flow of long, sustaining and soothing *ah*-sounds for several minutes.

» When you become more advanced you may do this exercise standing or sitting. When you have completed the exercise journal or draw your experience it. *Enjoy!*

Note: In the exercise described above we use open-mouth breathing in both the inhaling and exhaling breath, which provides optimal oxygen intake, maximising prana energy intake. Inhaling and exhaling through the nose will especially activate and stimulate the upper body. Nose breathing is necessary to filter and cleanse the air we breathe. When we are communicating or vocalising, we are not concerned about nose breathing.

> » Take a full deep breath now, several times. Are you surprised at the instant results? You feel great, right?
> » Further relax into letting your belly be big and expansive with a full deep breath. Now make an *ah*-sound or a sighing sound. Are you able to do that without tucking in your tummy muscles? Just take note of it and accept as you read on.

We hold our emotions and thoughts in our tummy muscles. *Being fully alive means being able to breathe with our tummy muscles.* Don't be afraid of using them, surprise yourself again and again. Breath is what we share with every human being. We all breathe air to exist. The more we breathe the more alive and intoxicated with life we become. When we cannot stop deep breathing because of pure excitement and because it feels so good, we become very alive. Deep breathing fertilises our mind and energises our entire physical and emotional body.

I used to sit in front of the computer for hours without paying attention to my breathing, which of course resulted in stress and overworking. Being on the internet is very demanding and literally takes our breath away. You may have thoughts like: *How efficiently or quickly can I check my emails today? How many deadlines do I have to meet by today or before the end of the week? If I don't check my emails today I will miss an important message and feel incomplete.* Do these thoughts sound familiar to you?

There is hope! Start establishing a relationship with breath

by listening to your own breath rhythm. Make sighing *ah*-sounds often and do not allow the computer energy to override your life or victimise you. This is a big task, but it's possible to achieve. It took me a while to master, but I am now able to stay energised when working in cyberspace. I do deep breathing

EXERCISE
Breathe fully to give and receive in harmony

This practice helps direct your intention to the breath rhythm, allowing you to embody a quality you wish to receive. Groundedness and manifestation come with an embodied breath. This exercise further trains your ability to surrender, let go and be in the flow of life.

» Lie down and listen to your natural inhaling and exhaling breaths. Focus on your inhaling breath and make it slightly longer than your exhaling breath. Think of a quality you would like to receive, for example 'joy'. Let each breath emerge into a joyous experience as you embody this quality.

» Use conscious, connected breathing; this means breathing in and out without any pause in between. This supports you in diving deeper and staying focused in a continuous flow. Practise for up to five minutes.

» Now focus on your exhaling breath, which you make slightly longer than your inhaling breath. Listen to what you want to let go of, an issue, pain or negative thought. Or focus on what you would like to manifest and express.

Practise for a maximum of five minutes. Remember to go slowly and stop the exercise if you experience strong discomfort or resistance. Let go on the exhale.

» Finish by connecting to your heartbeat. Let it speak to you through your breath. Connect to the heartbeat of the earth itself as you visualise being a part of Mother Earth's heartbeat. Dwell in this inspiration and image for a while before returning to the present.

» Variation: It's possible to start on the exhaling breath first and then the inhaling breath.

» This conscious breath exercise is excellent to practise before you get out of bed in the morning. Journal your experience or draw it. *Enjoy!*

consciously and often, I practise my aahing sound and I take lots of breaks.

I use various breathing exercises combined with sound work in my Soul Voice teaching, to access our deepest cellular memory. The breath, which is intentionally guided, supports and moves the emotional body and higher consciousness to the deepest layers of the subconscious. I also use different breathing techniques to allow the voice to come across more clearly in expression and

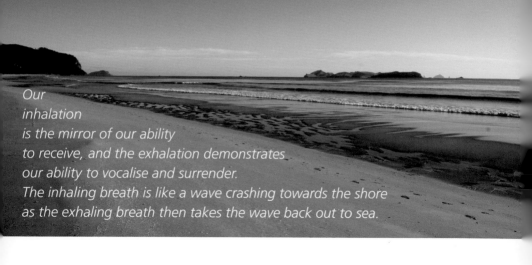

Our inhalation is the mirror of our ability to receive, and the exhalation demonstrates our ability to vocalise and surrender.
The inhaling breath is like a wave crashing towards the shore as the exhaling breath then takes the wave back out to sea.

Breathing fully makes the invisible prana energy manifest in waves of the body's natural bliss state.

communication. The voice becomes an extension of how well we are able to access and develop our breath capacity.

Yogis use breath to purify their inner temple — the body; they use breath control as a peaceful way to detach from the outer world. Some ascended masters have used breathing as an ultimate tool for coming into complete oneness with the divine, and to ascend consciously. Yogananda is a beautiful example of this.

Breath, heart and rhythm

The inhaling breath brings us into physical form and matter; it is our yin and female energy. It is our ability to be open, to receive, to contain, to grow. Our exhaling breath is our yang and male energy, which signifies the capacity to give, let go, express, vocalise, manifest. The inhaling and exhaling breath is a constant dance between the inner yin and the outer yang energy.

If the inhaling breath is shallow, we restrict our partaking of life. We live from a headspace afraid of really receiving, which creates not only muscular tension and 'armour', but also shuts down emotions and creative expression. When the inhaling breath is full and deep, it supports being supercharged, receiving abundance and being present in our body.

When the exhaling breath is controlled or pushed, we are holding on to something and we create struggle; we limit our potential. When the exhaling breath is freed it supports creative expression, letting-go processes and manifestation power.

As adults we breathe 26,000 times a day! Imagine what a difference it would make in your daily life if you lived a conscious breathing life.

We seem to be running out of breath so much of the time. We have been preoccupied in giving and not paying enough attention to receiving the breath.

I consciously breathe a full, deep breath. Everything is quiet around me, I feel calm and content. I listen to the sound of silence. I become aware of the sound of my own breath, the breath in and out of my nose and mouth. I breathe to communicate with the deepest part of my being — in the voice of silence. I observe my body and I witness my spirit. I am in the space between heaven and earth. I stop breathing for a moment until the next breath naturally arises. I lay on the grass for an extended time as I relax into listening to my own heartbeat, together with the heartbeat of our Mother Earth. My consciousness expands; there are no thoughts or feelings, only breath which unites me to earth, spirit and the inner voice. I dwell in meditation.

CHAPTER 9

Intuition & the embodied higher senses

Intuition is our knowing and not knowing.
Intuition is a wisdom
that requires no justification.
Intuition is our sense of being alert
to the unpredictable, in which state
we may discover our greatest qualities
in vibration of sound and light.

Imagine yourself at the top of a cliff, ready to take a freefall in complete trust and faith. I stand there again and again in that place of not knowing. I am asked to take this big jump if I want to be true to myself, to free myself from habitual living and awaken the spontaneity that is my birthright. In this quantum leap my intuition is stimulated and awakened. Being on the edge, I am always on my way to the next jump or in the midst of a new jump. The flight that takes me when I surrender and devote myself to my intuition stays alert and clear. I smell, I taste, I see, I feel, I hear. As I let my sensuous being be stimulated by these senses my intuition thrives and becomes more trustworthy, refined and elevated. I feel alive and whole.

A recent report on the senses from Howard Hughes Medical Institute, Maryland, USA, says:

Living with our senses gives us the greatest spirituality, as all higher senses become unified into intuition.

> We can recognize a friend instantly — full-face, in profile, or even by the back of his head. We can distinguish millions of shades of colour, as well as 10,000 smells. We can feel a feather as it brushes our skin, hear the faint rustle of a leaf. It all seems so effortless: we open our eyes or ears and let the world stream in. Yet anything we see, hear, feel, smell, or taste requires billions of nerve cells to flash urgent messages along cross-linked pathways and feedback loops in our brains, performing intricate calculations that scientists have only begun to decipher.

Researcher and author Penney Peirce says about intuition:

> The intuitive process is really a way of living, a way of aligning with what's truly real. Here are four facts about intuition: (1) With intuition, you know what you need to know, right when you need to know it. (2) When you look at the world intuitively, the question and answer exist together and arise in the same instant. (3) Intuition cuts through the normal limitations of time and space. (4) With intuition you learn that the process, not necessarily the answers, is the important thing.

Let intuition be your guide

Intuition is a non-rational state of consciousness; it is the spontaneous, limitless, timeless self. Intuition may be chaotic, wild and dreamy; it is a guide to the subconscious. Intuition brings us back to the original blueprint of knowingness. When we allow ourselves to give up control — either being in control or being controlled by others — and when we finally let go of having to analyse, be logical or know better to experience the freefall, then intuition can start to kick in.

Intuition fosters living without knowing; being in a void where everything is possible. It is a place which requires grounding and focus so that the information received can be manifested. It is a meditative space of non-linear perception.

Intuition is believing in your individuality, your higher self and your interpretation of things, instead of letting yourself be directed by rules, outer authorities, or structures which contradict inner truth.

Let your intuition soar by developing your senses and subtle sensitivity further. Let your wildest dreams find an outlet in art: painting, acting, sculpting, singing, sound healing and meditation, for example.

How do you recognise intuition in even the simplest activities? Our sensitivity is something we were born with so we can commune with all life forces. When we use our intuition we tap into a higher vibration that fuels our soul and wellbeing. I look into the eyes of a person I have just met, and I know this person; she or he seems so familiar, as though I have met this soul before.

➡ **TRY THIS:** Reflect and check in with yourself:
- » When did you last use your intuitive abilities and act on them?
- » How did that make a difference in your communication or activities?
- » Give yourself credit for your intuition.

When you doubt, or have difficulties at work or in a relationship, when you are up against personal problems, ask your intuition: *What shall I do now; how do I stop feeling stuck?* Take time to be still and meditative; trust that you know what you need to know and there will always be an answer. You are a divine instrument; intuition works in mysterious ways. There are no rights or wrongs, so send out to the universe what you desire and wish to attract and let it manifest by exploring your intuitive skills.

Life itself is intuitive art. In every moment, have the courage to live it.

We now proceed to the five senses on a physical–energetic level to deepen our experience of intuition.

The five higher senses

The senses give us a stronger experience of self, enhanced passion and innocence to all our endeavours. These delicious senses are related to our chakras, which are energetic vortices in the etheric body, a place where body and mind unite. The chakras correlate with the endocrine and the nervous systems. They can be contacted both in the front of the body and the back. Each chakra relates to a particular aspect of the human experience, and is a receptor of all information coming from our surroundings and from the cosmos.*

In this chapter we relate the five senses to the chakra system and to an additional sense, *intuition*. The physical five senses are: *smell,* related to the root chakra; *taste,* related to the hara chakra; *seeing,* related to the solar plexus chakra; *feeling,* related to the heart chakra, and *hearing,* related to the throat chakra. The primary location of smell is in the nose; the sense of taste — the mouth; the sense of seeing — the eyes; the sense of feeling — the heart, and the sense of hearing in the ears.

* The *Soul Voice* book explains each chakra and offers further information and practices.

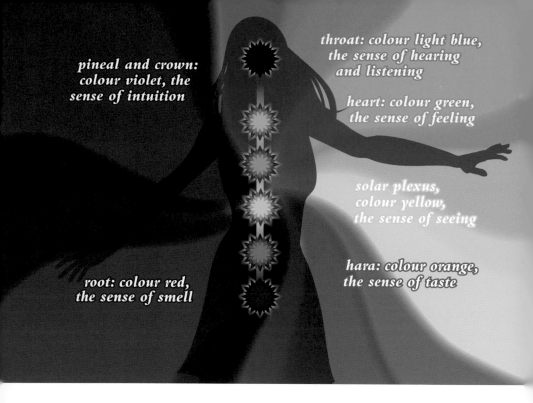

pineal and crown: colour violet, the sense of intuition

throat: colour light blue, the sense of hearing and listening

heart: colour green, the sense of feeling

solar plexus, colour yellow, the sense of seeing

hara: colour orange, the sense of taste

root: colour red, the sense of smell

The sense of smell

Smell has always been important in my life. Often I need to have a sense of smell to belong, and I may tune into a person's smell before I attempt communication. If there is an uncomfortable smell in a room I immediately change the energy by sounding and using sage, a Native American herb which is strongly cleansing. I often have a sense of smell associated with clients. When I enter into a person's energy field I may sense their soul-being through a distinct smell.

Smell opens us up to our gut instincts and our reptilian brain. Certain smells may stimulate our wellbeing, others may intoxicate or calm us. Many smells have become artificial, so we are not able to smell the origins of a particular thing. Putting chemicals in almost everything has strongly diluted the sense of smell. Smells can be so polluted they are a danger to our health. If you are in an environment or job where lots of chemicals are used, consider any changes you can make to this critical situation. Aromatherapy offers a wide variety of essential oils, each with a distinct smell for any given quality or atmosphere you wish to create.

The sense of smell relates to the root chakra, situated at the tailbone or the perineum; it is the chakra for grounding, manifestation and safety and is reflected in the colour red.

Mothers may recognise their babies by smell; newborns recognise their mothers by smell. Our sense of smell connects us to memory.

Smell stimulates instincts and a sense of feeling grounded. There are smells we could not live without because they uplift and inspire our creative expressions and thoughts. Take a deep breath now through your nose and take in the smell of your environment.

Take another deep breath and ask yourself if this is the right smell for you. Did you notice when you entered the room what smell the room had? The first step is to become conscious about smell.

I invite you to be aware of smell in various circumstances.

➡ TRY THIS:

» Smell a flower, essential oil or perfume which uplifts you.
» Smell a meal before and during eating to awaken your appetite and give greater pleasure in eating.
» Smell nature after a rain which pushes Mother Earth's plant kingdom to accelerate growth and smells.

Note: When working with the chakras, visualise a colour. You visualise the colour by feeling it. Colours will enhance the perception of all the senses.*

---

* For further information on this subject see the *Soul Voice* book.

Let smell intoxicate you

This exercise stimulates strong grounding; it gives you a sense of living in the body and belonging to the earth as your instinctive power is awakened more fully.

» Take a moment to fully relax and breathe deeply. Let your nostrils open wide and breathe in the smell of your environment. What are your body sensations? Take notice of them.

» Now add an attractive smell to your environment; light some incense or put perfume or essential oil on your skin. How does this affect you?

» Walk barefoot in nature; breathe the air fully in through your nose taking in the smell of nature.

» Choose a place to meditate on your root chakra energy, either in nature, or a room you have infused with an attractive smell. Breathe deeply into the root chakra, visualise and feel the red colour and let the smell further open up this chakra.

» Focus on inhaling through the nose, receiving the smell with each breath. On the exhale, express sounds that match the experience. Do this for up to five minutes.

» When nearing completion state the affirmation: *I listen to my instincts through the sense of smell and I allow myself to feel both intoxicated and calm in doing so.* Match the affirmation with sound frequencies to embody it. Listen to your intuitive insights and follow what you perceive.

» When ready listen further in silence before journalling or drawing the experience. Honour yourself for having embarked on a new awareness of developing the sense of smell. The more you use it the more it develops. *Enjoy!*

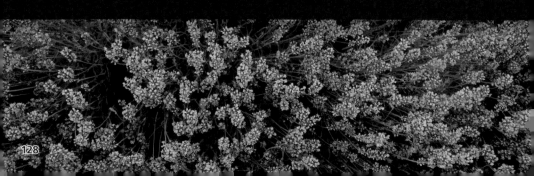

The sense of taste

We are constantly bombarded with seductive selections regarding our taste's desires. Although food most often gives us great pleasure and satisfaction it can easily be compensation or a substitute for something else. A dear friend and chef, Marc Boucher, founder of La Cuisine Sacre, expressed his concerns when he observed how people go to a restaurant to eat a three-course dinner and all they remember from the evening is what the conversation was about; they had no clue what they were actually putting into their mouths. Marc suggests we now and then take a day off from food and drink to allow our tummy a rest, which entails living on saliva only! This treat enhances the sensitivity of the saliva and activates a completely new perception of and receptivity to food. To schedule a 'saliva day' is a pretty hard task for most of us to follow; however it gives great benefits. By becoming more sensitive to our saliva glands we are better able to control unhealthy eating habits.

You may start by eating mindfully in silence, or having a fruit day or a juice day once a month. Because we often over eat, our sense of taste is diminished. The campaigns about what you should and should not eat illustrate just how much we have lost our intuitive sense of what is good for us. *We are often lost in consuming rather than using discernment.* Eating is an art form; let it be shown in your own dining room.

The enjoyment of taste relates to the chi-centre — the hara chakra a couple of inches below the navel — and is reflected in the colour orange. It stimulates pleasure, appetite, sexuality, creativity, flow, movement, action and play. Taste is associated with our whole digestive system. How we treat our digestive system is of high importance to our wellbeing, our voice, stamina and metabolism. When we cultivate a healthy relationship with our body and what it needs, it knows what and how much to eat. Taste becomes an original sense of mindfulness and natural satisfaction, which serves our highest purpose. We may choose organic food and bless the food by, for example, sounding before eating, in gratitude to the origins of what we consume and in appreciation of those who prepared the food. Food can become orgasmic when served and enjoyed with utmost sensitivity involving all the senses. *So slow down to enjoy what you eat!*

When we start to develop a higher sense of taste we begin to enjoy life's many pleasures to an even greater extent. We may use the sense of taste without engaging the digestive system and experience a different approach to taste.

➡ TRY THIS:

» Taste an apple without eating it.
» Taste the 'sweet fruit' of sexuality without having sex.
» Give a client session where the sense of taste guides the healing.

We also use the sense of taste to organise and decorate our home for example. The way we dress originates from our sense of taste. I experience when my sense of taste is balanced that I am fuelled with a special satisfaction; not because I have eaten a meal but because my expression is in a harmonious flow full of inner vitality, and my digestive system is at ease and in peace. It is from this satisfaction that my creativity has a great foundation to flourish.

))) EXERCISE
Slow motion eating and infusion of higher consciousness

Conscious eating as described here allows you to be nurtured on many levels and to change any old habits concerning the art of eating. By practising this eating exercise regularly you train a more subtle sense of taste

PART ONE

» Smell your food and look at it with joy and gratitude; take a moment to breathe in and taste your saliva; sound in anticipation of the glorious food you are about to eat. Then, when your saliva is highly stimulated and your sense of taste fully awake, start eating. As you eat each mouthful, take less food than you would normally. Chew for longer so that the food becomes liquid before you swallow it. Follow the same procedure with your next mouthful, starting with smelling and looking at the dish and noticing your saliva.

» Listen to your stomach as it becomes fuller. Feel the great pleasure of eating consciously. Stop eating before you feel completely full.

» Notice your saliva now and sense the difference from when you started the meal.

» Move away from the table where you have enjoyed your food. Listen to your hara chakra and be still. When you are ready say the affirmation aloud or silently: *I am sustained and nourished on all levels by the food I enjoy.* Visualise and feel the colour orange.

» When you are ready, match the affirmation with sound frequencies that embody the affirmation and the colour; listen to intuitive insights. Enjoy practising slowness.

» Listen further in silence before journaling or drawing the experience. *Enjoy!*

PART TWO

» Make a journal of everything you eat and drink over the next three days. Also take note of the atmosphere in which you enjoy your meals, as well as the pace of eating.

» On the fourth day look at your journal in acceptance and come into a quiet space. State an intention; for example, 'I nourish, nurture and sustain myself on all levels through my conscious eating. I am healthy and I always know what is best for me to eat.'

» Sound the affirmation into the hara chakra for a while. Then, infuse your body with a transparent orange vibration, drink in its etheric elixir and mana. Contact the nervous system in your spine, and continue sounding as you visualise the sounds flowing up and down your spinal cord.

» When you have finished, rest in silence and peace. Let yourself be fulfilled by the sound vibrations which are healing your digestive system and your relationship to taste. Listen to any intuitive insights.

» When ready, journal or draw the experience. Honour yourself for having embarked on a new awareness into the importance of developing the sense of taste. The more you use it the more it develops. *Enjoy!*

The sense of seeing

The sense of seeing is the most used of all senses. What a wonderland of visual impressions and expressions we surround ourselves with and take part in. Our eyes, being the gateway to see externally as well as the windows to our soul, are infused with extraordinary visualisation and imagination. However, indulging in the visual may make us blind to what we really need. How do we choose what is essential for us and what are our needs in this over-exposed visual panorama?

The visual media, for example, easily seduces us. We can be in any possible reality in a split of a second, hypnotised and caught up in images and realities that may not serve our greatest interest.

Seeing is related to the solar plexus chakra, which is situated below the sternum and reflected in the colour yellow. It is our expression of inner power and decision making, boundary setting, manifestation of power and passion. In seeing, most of us have the tendency to make an unconscious, habitual movement forward with our eyes. This habitual movement is forced; we strain our eyes and our brain, which may result in unhealthy eye conditions and problems.

Looking into the computer screen for too many hours is another example of forcing. Choosing consciously is a quality related to the solar plexus. I recommend you choose to look at something calming between online communications to stay relaxed and clear.

➡ **TRY THIS:** Take a moment to stop reading this book, close your eyes and cover them with your hands. Sense the back of your neck where you can rest and dwell in your consciousness. The latter is called the upper visual cortex, the centre for processing dreamtime and for relaxing strain you put on yourself.

» What did you discover? Did your eyes get a rest?
» Trust whatever you experienced and train this often to avoid straining the eyes.

Seeing within and beyond

This practice gives a deep relaxation to the eyes and thought processes, and an overall sense of renewed wellbeing. The exercise focuses your ability to choose images and thus not be overwhelmed by the visual inner world.

» Choose an object, for example a candle, a crystal, a flower or any sacred object, with which to have an eye-gazing experience.

» Start to look at the chosen object as you relax into an awareness of the upper visual cortex area. Practise for five minutes or more. You may experience images, body sensations, past memories, colours, or you may just have a pure experience of seeing the physical object. Trust and accept your unique way of perceiving. Do not hold on to any of the images, let them flow in and out of your awareness. Sound to filter what is most important for you to experience.

» Contact your solar plexus chakra area. Visualise and feel the colour yellow. Allow this centre to further support you as you continue sounding. When ready take time to listen in silence.

» Now close your eyes and sink into the third eye area between the eyebrows. You may have strong visual images coming to you; trust them and allow them to pass as on a movie screen. Give sounds to any images you perceive as important. Take one image at a time. If you have no visual images, trust that seeing can be a sense of knowingness and be supported by the sense of feeling. Trust what you feel.

» When complete, come back to gaze at the object for a couple of minutes. Journal or draw the experience. Honour yourself for having embarked on a new awareness of the importance of developing the sense of inner seeing. The more you use it the more it develops. *Enjoy!*

Peter Grunwald says in his ground-breaking book *Eyebody*:

> The upper visual cortex has the potential to integrate the entire visual system by means of what I call conscious depth perception. Conscious depth perception is a mental direction which creates coordination and integration of all regions of the brain. Through this mechanism a dynamic balance is achieved within the entire system that results in clarity of sight and thinking alike.

Close your eyes often to give them a rest. Dwell in the upper visual vortex area. Give sounds to your eyes to relax them and nurture them, the external and internal gateway to the soul.

When we look into another person's eyes for an extended time we identify strongly with the soul. We are drawn to look behind the mask, beyond physical impressions and appearance.

What we ultimately give energy to, will grow. We need to train our visual capability, choosing the images of importance and value to us, as the inner world is a huge storage house of recollections and unlimited images. Let the visual world serve you and not confuse you; let it stimulate your dreams and visions. Your higher sense of seeing, behind ordinary and physical reality, opens you to embracing clairvoyant skills.

The sense of feeling

In the movie *The Living Matrix* scientists confirm:

> The heart has its own intrinsic nervous system which can sense, feel, remember and process information that is independent from the brain. We have always thought of the information-input system being entirely in the brain and we are now discovering that the heart receives information first and then relays it to the brain, which then coordinates it back to the body. Studies have shown that the heart responds faster than the brain to outside stimulation, being the master organ to imprint information into the body-field.

Emotions hold our life tapestry. They enable us to flow and change direction at any given moment. Emotions are in all our blood cells and our billions of nerves. Stop lolling about and being so

EXERCISE

Feeling is healing

By practising the following exercise you get a stronger awareness of the feeling sense. It allows you to locate feeling through tangible body sensations and stimulates greater perception of the heart. Feeling is a foundation for the other senses to grow stronger.

» Take a moment to relax and observe your breath. Consciously let go on the exhale and breathe in with awareness on the inhale breath.

» Contact any part of your body where you feel something, either a sensation you like or a sensation of discomfort or irritation. When you have located that part of your body, make sounds representing what you are feeling. Put your hands on the area if possible. Start to exaggerate the sounds as you allow the feeling sensation to become stronger. Listen to the sound itself and let yourself be guided to the next sound and so on. If you are not able to feel, play with the emotion, 'fake it till you make it', it which means util you are able to feel it for real.

» Contact your heart chakra area and listen and communicate with the heart as you visualise and feel the colour green. Let the colour guide you to express what you feel. Say this feeling aloud and match it with sound frequencies. Feel the feelings in various parts of your body and choose one part to intensify sound into. Let this develop intuitively.

» When you are complete, sit in silence for a moment and feel the new sensation emerging from your cells. Be grateful for what you have learnt and observed. Listen to your intuitive insights and follow through on what you received.

» Draw or write about the new sensation in your body and the associated consciousness. Honour yourself for having embarked on a new awareness of developing the sense of feeling. The more you use it the more it develops. *Enjoy!*

hard on yourself by ignoring the feeling that is communicating a message to you! Invite yourself to become more alive and vibrant by exploring emotions!

The feeling sense is in the heart chakra at the centre of the chest, and is reflected in the colour green; it is the centre of compassion, self-love and interconnectedness. It is the chakra from which all life pulsates and originates. To live life from a heart-centred awareness is the direction we are asked to move into.

Feeling is intimacy, feeling is allowing to receive and be touched. Our hands function as our creative antennae, directly connected to our heart's resonance. Touch is confirmation of connectedness and belongingness. Women especially are strongly connected to touch, and the ramifications of touch. What can a touch from a loved one or friend reveal in a moment of doubt or frustration! Touch is an immediate response that acknowledges the sense of feeling. Touch strengthens feelings of safety and allows the recipient to sink deeper into trust and receptivity.

➡ **TRY THIS:** Touch anything that feels good to touch, bringing awareness to the heart:

» How different is the sensation of touching silk clothes compared to touching a tree?
» Which parts of your body get stimulated when you touch a texture that ignites other senses as well, for example caressing an animal's fur?
» Touch in such a way that you strongly feel your emotions; play with both soft touch and firm touch and sense the different body sensations. Celebrate being alive by choosing to touch more often.
» Take a walk barefoot on the wet grass in the morning dew.
» Take the next nature adventure without shoes to enhance the sense of feeling.

Training being clair-sentient is a part of becoming a skilful Soul Voice practitioner: by bringing the soul's resonance into embodiment through emotional equilibrium we are able to reach far higher, to the voice's awakening potentials and healing abilities.

When feeling is expressed and freed you no longer feel separated. You train the freedom to feel by stopping many times during the day to check in with any body sensations. If you are stuck and cannot feel anything do something about it. Contact a part of your body where you may at least feel a tiny sensation; when feeling gets acknowledged it starts to grow.

See Chapter 4 for more in-depth information on emotions.

The sense of hearing and listening

How often do we hear something, but are not able to fully take it in; to listen, to filter, to select and to respond properly to what we actually hear? I have developed a series of exercises that enable students to delete unwanted voices and noises in the cellular memory through listening to the inner voice, which enables the practitioner to diagnose. Discernment and boundary-setting techniques are necessary to differentiate between what belongs to us while staying vulnerable and sensitive.

The sense of hearing originates in the throat chakra, situated at the throat and reflected in the colour light blue; this is our main centre for expression, communication, freedom, ability to synergise duality and surrender to divine will. The skill of listening enables us to come to the essence by using sound frequencies to heighten our consciousness and to penetrate to the core of all things. Our

EXERCISE
Listening within

This exercise trains meditative awareness and helps you differentiate and release external sounds. It enhances your listening skills, and enables you to filter information and make the right choices.

» Take a moment to sink into yourself through deep breathing. Close your eyes. Listen to any external sounds. What are these sounds? Are you hearing the wind, or birdsong; do you hear traffic noise, construction noise or the sound of people's chatter? Allow yourself to listen to these external sounds one at a time.

» For each sound notice how you filter it: Does it stay outside your body or do you take it in? Experience how it feels to take a pleasant sound into a specific area of your body, and then how it feels to take in an unpleasant sound.

» Make some neutralising *ah*-sounds for a couple of minutes to your throat chakra area to free yourself from all sounds and noises. Feel and sound the colour light blue. Continue until you sense a feeling of peace and harmony.

» Go to the area below your third eye (between your eyebrows), where there is an 'inner silence point'. Listen to your internal self, to your heart beating, your tummy rumbling, the sound of your breath, the sound of your blood flowing through your veins and any other subtle internal sounds. Listen with your whole body. Sense it as one pulsating, listening organ, as you awaken billions of listening nerves. Listen in relaxation, surrender and confidence.

» Bring your own unique sounding music into this exquisite sensation and celebrate your listening.

» When complete, listen in silence to the part of your body you heard your inner voice most clearly. Trust wherever you intuit this to be. Take time to relax and listen for an extended time. Do not think, simply be. Whatever your listening experience is, trust and honour it.

» When complete journal any insights. Honour yourself for having embarked on a new awareness into the importance of developing the sense of listening. The more you use it the more it develops. *Enjoy!*

hearing starts with our ears; however, when we develop our sense of hearing, both externally and internally, we hear and listen with our whole being. Every cell in our body is an ear.

When we are able to listen without being bothered by the busy monkey-mind, we start to develop intuitive listening skills, called clairaudiant skills.

Chapter 3 gives you more in-depth information on the art of listening.

Intuition and the five senses

Intuition is a synergy of our mastery of the five senses combined with our level of attunement, growth and development of subtle energies, including the chakras. Intuition is an all encompassing energy. It is both a feminine and a masculine energy. Although I sense intuition as nestled in the two upper chakras — the pineal chakra and the crown chakra, intuition is indeed a synergy of all chakras and our whole system's refinement.

Soar over the endless river of intuitive perception to the kingdom of God's omnipresence.
~ Paramahansa Yogananda

So allow the senses, together with the chakras' subtle energies, to communicate with you. Reflect on your inner feminine/masculine balance which relates to how well you are in contact with intuition. All creation is born of the feminine principle, and all manifestation is born of the masculine principle. Creation and manifestation cannot be separated. Intuition is an introvert yin energy and an extravert yang energy. When we are able to surrender to the yin and the yang as one, from within our intuition rejoices in clarity and newness, a divine spark of wisdom and creative expression.

EXERCISE

Intuition and the chakras

This practice will synthesise the seven chakras and support balance and overall wellbeing. Equalising the seven chakras supports strong grounding and boundary-setting. It strengthens intuition and nourishes your inner yin and yang with renewed stamina, beingness and vision.

» Sit in a relaxed meditative body position. Contact the root chakra. Open yourself to receive the qualities of groundedness, sacredness and safety by sounding these qualities into the root chakra. At the same time visualise the colour red. Bring in the new consciousness of smell from the earlier exercise.

» After five minutes or more of self-healing to the root chakra dwell in silence to integrate and to be with what is.

» Contact your hara chakra. Open yourself to receive the qualities of pleasure, play and flow by sounding these qualities into the hara chakra, together with the colour orange. Bring in the new consciousness of taste from the earlier exercise.

» After five minutes or more of self-healing to the hara chakra, dwell in silence to integrate and to be with what is.

» Contact the solar plexus chakra. Open yourself to receive the qualities of passion, inner power and boundary setting by sounding these qualities into the solar plexus chakra to the best of your ability, together with the colour yellow. Bring in your new consciousness of seeing from the earlier exercise.

» After five minutes or longer of self-healing to the solar plexus chakra,

dwell in silence to integrate and to be with what is.

» Contact the heart chakra. Open yourself to receive the qualities of self-love, compassion and interconnectedness by sounding these qualities into the heart chakra to the best of your ability together with the colour green. Bring in the new consciousness of feeling and touch from the previous exercise.

» After five minutes or longer of self-healing to the heart chakra, dwell in silence to integrate and to be with what is.

» Contact the throat chakra. Open yourself to receive the qualities of authentic expression, clear communication and divine will by sounding these qualities into the throat chakra to the best of your ability, together with the colour light blue. Bring in the new consciousness of listening from the previous exercise.

» After about five minutes of self-healing to the throat chakra, dwell in silence to integrate and to be with what is.

» Contact the pineal chakra situated in the third eye area, as well as the crown chakra, situated at the top of your head. Let your consciousness, supported by your breath, alternate between the pineal and the crown chakra, weaving an energy between these two chakras of clarity, beingness, devotion, surrender and oneness. Visualise and feel the colour violet.

>> Bring the essence of what you experienced in the five previous chakras into focus and weave it all into the pineal and crown chakras. Relax into the sensation and stay in inner stillness for a while.

>> When you are ready ask your intuition to guide you to any attributes you may wish to deepen. Match the experience with sound. Allow yourself breaks to better integrate the transformation

>> When ready, listen and be still. If you drift away, pay attention to your breath and ground yourself. Surrender.

>> When you want to return to your new awakening consciousness, move from your pineal-crown area to the spine, where you can let your breath move down the spinal cord. Allow any spontaneous sounding be expressed.

>> When complete return to your heart. Listen and be. Take time to integrate and journal the experience.

>> Do a grounded activity before you continue your day. *Enjoy!*

*Everyone has a purpose in life, a unique gift
to share with humanity.
When we allow the greatest potential
of purpose and intuition to extend to selfless
service to others we come to experience bliss
and ecstasy, the meaning of life.
We become fulfilled in Spirit,
in action and in devotion.*

CHAPTER 10

Nature is our home

Nature is calling us to listen.
Nature is calling us to receive and to surrender.
Nature brings us back to our roots
and our ancestral connections;
to remember Her abundance every moment;
to offer service to those precious elements:
the earth, water, fire and air that sustain us.
These are our building blocks of existence, our teachers.
May we take action which honours the great Creator.
May we give back to Her a thousandfold
in respect and sustainability, in eternal gratitude.

Native Americans tell us that when we forget to send gratitude to the sun, it may one day not appear. We cannot give enough appreciation to the all-life-giving sun. On a holiday with my husband at the northernmost part of Denmark, Skagen in Jutland, we were witness to a very impressive and beautiful sunset ritual. Each evening the inhabitants of the village, including tourists, gathered to watch the sun setting over the ocean 'Skagerrak'. As it did so, everyone clapped their hands in appreciation and acknowledgment. Within minutes after the sun had set into the ocean, everybody was gone. Kevin and I continued to sit on the beach in silence, seeing the amazing colour and cloud formations in the after-sunset light. At a given moment we both simultaneously started to sound our prayers in gratitude and in reverence.

Nature, the true awakener

When we ignore living in true relationship to the earth and do not treat it as sacred, we continue to destroy the environment. The greed and materialism that govern Planet Earth, have come to a big crisis point. A new evolutionary change is needed, a realisation that all life on earth is of one and the same spirit. The destruction and greed can only go so far, before Mother Earth reacts strongly and clearly for humanity to wake up. Global summits on climate change still do not seem to have the action needed in place. However, it is the individual wake-up call that matters now. It is every human being's responsibility to choose to live with reverence and sustainability in all their actions. To live in love and mindfulness and to treat one another as soul-brothers and soul-sisters. To share the abundance that we are, no matter how much or how little we have to offer. It is never too late to awaken this innate wisdom of how to live on earth in a sacred way — in faith, grace and trust.

Nature reveals and expresses itself through an organic growth process which is interrelated with the human psyche. The grand power of shamans originate from their living with nature, knowing its secrets in continuous communication and obedience,

*In ancient times the wise beings saw themselves
as a reflection of the universe.
They studied the star system and nature
to understand the great Creator, the great
mystery and themselves.
Communication with nature brings us to
an unconditional place within our soul.
It permeates us with its glory of abundance.
It shows us how to live in fearlessness,
agelessness and detachment, and brings us the
greatest joy in confirmation of eternal life.*

deep inner listening and surrendering to truth. They cultivate the wisdom and power of Nature Herself.

The four elements are interwoven into this — there would be no life on Planet Earth if one of the elements was missing. Earth, water, fire and air are not only in our environment, but also within our physical human constellation. The elements' myriad compositions give us a wide spectrum of climates, bringing both great challenges and immeasurable pleasures, but always the ability to adapt to extremes where humans exist.

Nature awakens us to greater truth as it pushes us to listen. The earthquakes, hurricanes, cyclones and tsunamis that are becoming more frequent on our precious blue-green planet are part of the uncontrollable power nature shows us. Nature is in charge and guiding us, awakening humanity with its voice of radical changes to such an extent that our egocentricity will have to surrender. The wake-up call is massive. Mother Nature knows what she needs to do to realign and to balance.

We are all a part of this process, consciously or unconsciously. The planet is a living micro- and macro-cosmic entity. It holds the cellular memories of all creatures and acts according to humanity's actions and behaviors. Humanity needs to *listen* and to *surrender*, to remove any unhealthy habitual consciousness and belief system, take head of our authentic destiny and allow nature to realign itself.

We may move more gracefully through the earth's changes by completely trusting in nature. We will have to surrender our fear and control, surrender to our own inner process and power, and to our collective evolution. Wake up to compassion! We need to purify our souls and bodies, and serve humanity in accordance with nature's balance.

It is more important than ever for each of us to focus on inner work, on complete authenticity at all levels, and on connection to the heart of all life, Source itself.

Manifest a lifestyle that is in accordance with nature's prescribed laws. This is everyone's responsibility. We are all a part of this living conscious planet. It becomes more and more evident that what *you* express as truth influences not only yourself, your family, your community and your immediate surroundings but also the entire planet as conscious energy.

➡ TRY THIS: Reflect and meditate on the following questions:
» Why are you here?
» What is your service to humanity?
» How can *you* live with more passion, faith and joy?
» How can you be more in contact with nature and express your gifts?
» How can you be an example to others?
» How can you be a part of healing the elements and nature now?
» How can you take initiative to act — individually and collectively?

The compassion we have towards ourselves and for the planet is hugely accentuated each time we are shaken by a natural catastrophe. It affects us of course more strongly when it is in our own nation. However it is evident that no matter where the wake-up call is happening all humanity is affected in one or another way. This awakens our compassion and good-will so that we may come to understand the deeper and ultimate meaning of 'We are all one'.

As the February earthquake hit Christchurch, my heart was struck with a deep compassion. For the first time I truly felt a citizen of Aotearoa New Zealand. I sensed on a cellular level that my nation, my next-door neighbours, had been seriously hurt. I asked myself, *What can I do?* After hours of intense sound healing to Christchurch I knew my calling was to offer a free Soul Voice workshop in that city, in all humbleness and in service. It eventually became two one-day workshops with 60 participants attending. I was guided to go very slowly and gently in all practices, to allow them to process their traumatic experiences, step by step. The group process was supported by powerful Soul Voice practitioners assisting everyone.

We *can* make a difference! Our intentional sounds do permeate, and soothe, giving hope and faith to inner awakening and

transformation. They touch everything: the land, the people, the animals, the elements, the unseen forces. Like the rising Phoenix in the fire of transformation, I felt the compassionate calling to that voice which shakes, yields, soothes and transforms the hurt of old patterns into new consciousness and higher frequencies.

A statement from one of the participant still resonates in my being: 'We sounded like in the movie, *As it is in Heaven!* We have found our voice again here in Christchurch, and I feel we can find the heart of this city, which I sense we have never had before, by using our voices and sounds.'

Earth spirit

The earth is Gaia, the Great Mother. Everything that exists is born out of the Great Mother. She carries the cellular memory of all that has gone before us. Since Spirit can only be made manifest into matter through Her, She contains the seed within Her. She is the great mystery, the Source of all life, the Creator and Creation.

Earth is the fertility, the complexity and the duality of all that is, the nourishment, the life-giver and the death-bringer, our ancestral bones, the remembrance of all knowledge, wisdom and strength. She shows us an ecstatic symphony of mystical cycles and transformations, a flow of darkness and light, a passionate dance of extremes and changes, exotic gardens of colours, lusciousness and shapes that have us bow in awe to Creation. She is the roundness and the fertility, the cycles of death and rebirth, embraced in eternal beauty, stability and renewal.

I am in the midst of it — how could I not be? Nature pushes my creativity to blossom even further, it heightens my awareness as it brings me relaxation, focused intention and a devotion to Source always. As I walk our land in Coromandel, New Zealand, on the dewy grass in the early morning I express in intuitive sounding my honour to the land, its history and ancestors. I am again filled with this ecstatic feeling of remembrance and gratitude, a sensation of true belonging, a confirmation that spirit is truly pervading everything and everywhere. Nature is home.

Tree spirit

Tane Mahuta, Lord of the Forest, is a 2000-year-old New Zealand kauri. When I visited it I felt this majestic ancient tree's presence several kilometres away and became instantly filled with hope and strength. Tane Mahuta is a confirmation of beingness — this gigantic tree has been alive since Christ walked on earth. Imagine we have these ancient 'tall beings' among us, living and breathing subtle remembrance. How can we stop and reflect with them and let them teach us their wisdom?

Trees are a part of nature's big beings. I am in awe of their groundedness. Take a moment to ponder that thought and reflect on how trees may be able to assist you in your daily life.

When I approach a significant tree, especially a tree I already have a personal connection to, I first hear it from a distance. It communicates with me on an inner plane, if I truly listen. I have the utmost respect for trees. They radiate a unique stability and solidness which always make my spine strengthen and my heart expand. I stand there in front of it, honouring its shape, and its roots penetrating deep into the earth. I think about how I can

better stabilise my connection to the earth itself by letting the tree be my teacher. I honour its uprightness and core strength as I contact my own spine and nervous system and pray that it will endure with me under all circumstances. I honour the crown of the tree, as I allow it to arouse my consciousness to soar with the vision. I sense my crown and my consciousness are only able to expand when I honour my roots and my grounding. I communicate with the tree as if it is an old, wise friend I am

EXERCISE

Into the centre of the earth

This practice may give you a renewed relationship to the great
Mother Earth. It may unravel ancient memories, uplift you to
belonging and reverence, and to living in grace and gratitude.

» Position yourself close to the earth. If
you live in a multi-storeyed building,
trust that you can reach the earth
beneath you through intentional
visualisation. Consider practising in
nature, and notice the difference
compared with practising indoors.

» Start by setting an intention of coming
into contact with the earth element
more strongly. Sit or lie down, and take
some deep breaths. Surrender and just
be. Listen to the inner sound of your
heartbeat and relax even more. You
may experience a floating sensation
as you let your consciousness be
completely free of thoughts. Feel the
earth beneath you support and sustain
you. Focus on your breathing and take
a sense of the earth into your cells.

» Now, let your consciousness sink into
the earth. You are travelling further and
further into the earth itself. Let yourself
fall without resistance; trust that the
journey is safe. Match your intention
with your sounds.

» Imagine you are deep inside the earth.
Experience its red colour. There is
heat, warmth and space for you in this
universe of darkness.

» Listen to the memory of the earth.
What is She telling you? What are
you remembering? How is your
subconscious revealing information
to you — ancestral memories, images
from your life story or other lifetimes?
Receive in trust whatever form the
insights and wisdom appear.

» Be open to any form of sounding that
may support your embodiment and
bring you further into your essence.

» When complete, start to travel back
slowly, so that all the sensations and
information you have gathered in will
be held in your body's memory and
subconscious.

» Let yourself be lifted up. As you come
close to the earth's surface; sense a
network of roots surrounding you. Take
this sensation in and experience the red
colour. Start to sound powerfully the
experience you have gone through. Let
it ground you and become real, as you
gradually come back to the here and
now.

» When you feel complete, return to
consciousness. Make the transition by
taking a slow-motion walk, focusing
your awareness in your chi-centre.
Journal the whole experience. *Enjoy!*

meeting again. I tell stories that have importance to me or I ask for an answer to my prayers, whatever moves me or concerns me in the moment. I find rest and peace in simply listening together with the tree, either sitting against the trunk, lying beside the tree or standing with my front or back to it. Insights easily return to me. When I leave, I always give it something in return; it may be a hug of gratitude, I may give thanks by simply touching it with my hands, with a prayer, or I may kiss the tree or I leave it with some of my saliva. I always walk taller, yet more humble, after my encounter with trees.

Stone spirit

I am lying on a rock that may be millions of years old, imagine! What is there to do but surrender to the mighty rock so ancient, solid and contained, wise and beautiful beyond understanding? What is there to express but the song of ancient remembrance and gratitude? I lie face down to listen; I start to resonate sounds which make me sink deeper and deeper into the centre of myself, in tears of recognition, wonder and joy.

I recommend that the next time you wish for a rock encounter, lie down on the rock and listen, either face-up or face-down. Let yourself be carried away into the unknown, in confidence and in embrace.

Tree support

This practice brings strong groundedness, solidity, and creates a space for anchoring unconditional support and wisdom. It opens up the heart to trust, perseverance and abundance.

» Choose a tree. Look at it from root to crown and honour its existence. Look into your heart and acknowledge that you need both the root and the crown connection within you to be solid and in balance.

» Face the tree and secure your contact with it. Receive its strength, endurance and power by breathing deeply. Be quiet from within.

» Sense which part of your body needs attention. Do you have any pains or discomfort? Let's say it is your solar plexus area. Start breathing rhythmically and focus on long inhaling and exhaling breaths by expanding your abdomen muscles. Imagine your feet are rooted to the ground. Pull the energy from the roots of the tree into your feet and from there into your legs, and up to your solar plexus. Hold your breath for a moment, then exhale into the trunk of the tree from the solar plexus. Let go completely and imagine yourself inside the trunk, with your awareness going down into the roots in the earth.

» Repeat the above excercise several times until you feel at ease and energised.

» On an exhale, let your voice express a 'letting go', a release of any pain, discomfort or joy. Continue with the same excercise and let the tree give you all you need to receive.

» When you are ready to stop, express sounds of harmony and gratitude.

» Contact your heart and what you perceive as the heart of the tree. Visualise the hearts meeting and connecting. Stay in gratitude.

» Take time in silence to integrate any messages and information this tree connection has given you. *Enjoy!*

Stone is our first ancestor. It holds the building blocks of life. Without stone we would not be. It carries the story of the beginning of all and the seed of everything that follows.

~ **Barry Bradsfield**, author of *The Four Winds*

I was taking some integration time on a beautiful beach in Australia, right after a Soul Voice training, when I noticed two eagles soaring high in the sky. As they came closer they began to dance and weave together. I watched in wonder as they swooped down just above the water, their wings contracting and expanding, as they came closer in a direct line towards me. They began their ascent only metres away from me, and changed their direction to land in their nest, among the trees on the other side of the beach. Something encouraged me to walk along the beach close to where the eagles had landed. I then came to a place far away from other people. I sat on a large rock and gazed at the ocean. I saw a tribal elder dance and sing to the land in a vision. I felt that the land longed to hear those songs again. I began to sound, suddenly ancient songs poured out of my soul in complete love, surrender and honour. When the songs stopped, I sat in silence once again. I looked up and the two eagles were just a few metres in front of me, dancing and weaving around each other. I was asked to look around for the gift the land and her custodians were giving me. I was drawn to a beautifully coloured rock, covered in shades of orange. I picked it up. I was surprised to see a face looking back at me. It almost looked like someone had carved out eyes, a nose, lips, ears and hair. This was no ordinary rock, there was something very special about it, like it had been used in ceremonies long ago, but even more surprising was the knowing that inside the rock lived a being. I placed the rock carefully in my bag, after having asked permission to bring it with me. I thanked the land, the custodians and the eagles for all I had experienced. I felt the need to meditate with the rock, though some part of me thought I was being silly. A few weeks later a Shamanic teacher confirmed a soul had entered the rock and is a female. This experience has taught me many things, but most of all it has taught me all of creation does speak and all we have to do is sit in silence and listen. ~ Dorianne Daniels

Water spirit

Russian researchers and scientists made a DVD called *Water*:

The implications go beyond the solar system, suggesting that water has the ability to convey messages faster than light, perhaps linking water with the absolute. Water is so unique, and so profound. All its miraculous properties are still awaiting to be discovered.

Water is essential for our existence, and we consist of at least 70 percent water ourselves. Before we were born we spent nine months in the womb floating in embryonic fluid. The spirit of the waters embraces us with fluidity, flexibility and purification; a creative force of magnetism, emotions and birth, a connection to our subconscious depths, the unknown and the process of letting go and detaching. Water has a yielding effect and washes away our disharmony, distress or disorder as it enables our charity and

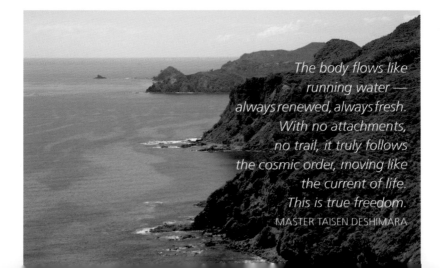

The body flows like running water — always renewed, always fresh. With no attachments, no trail, it truly follows the cosmic order, moving like the current of life. This is true freedom.
MASTER TAISEN DESHIMARA

Water cleanser

This exercise brings you in contact with the water element and the qualities of power, purification, yielding, flexibility and sensuality. It allows you to be in the now in an eternal wave of beingness of true power and wisdom.

» Take a bowl of water, bless it, then dip your fingers into it. With a finger, stroke your body anywhere you carry tension or pent-up energy.

» Direct your consciousness to the water in your body. Praise it with your presence and love. Sound to the water inside you; let it communicate to you and ask which areas of your life you need to flow more gracefully. Then express the sounds of the various characters of water — from powerfully pulsating to rhythmical soothing. Be cleansed, be dissolved, be purified.

» Go to the coast to learn from the sound of the ocean and its transformational powers. Find a spot to sit and listen to the waves. Listen until you become absorbed in the sound itself. Merge with the sound and half-close your eyes while you stare at the water. When you feel complete, cover your face with your hands for a while. Listen within and trust any messages you may receive.

» When complete with either the first step or the second step, make a drawing and journal the experience. *Enjoy!*

Inner fire is an element of transformation and great passion. It is the energy, that creates the spark of action, if we are out of tune with our surroundings or if we feel numb. The greater you nourish your inner flame, the brighter it radiates; the more passion and enthusiasm you have in your service to humanity, the grander your success. As Gandhi says:

> The best way to find yourself is to lose yourself in the service of others.

Let your burning passion and fire bring you home.

Air spirit

The air we breathe carries us to any desired destination, either on the physical plane or in our imagination. The air acts as a sword of protection, an arrow of communication, a feather of freedom. The air greatly influences the other three elements with its power and unpredictable nature. The air is uncontrollable as it caresses you, stirs you up, calms you and gives you connection to the infinite. It cannot be caught, but it gives life and movement to the fire, the waters, the trees and the earth.

Air is the invisible element that energetically supports our dreams and visions to manifest as it heightens our consciousness. Ride the waves of prana energy with your breath and allow guidance to communicate with you through the inner voice. Dive into the mystery of the air to become a part of its soul. Let your voice be infused by the air you breathe, as the air itself is the medium of all sounds. Air is the substance that allows us to fly as the winged ones — soar with the wind to reach unlimited potentials and freedom.

> The gulls who scorn perfection for the sake of travel go nowhere, slowly. Those who put aside travel for the sake of perfection go anywhere, instantly.
> ~ **Richard Bach**, *Jonathan Livingston Seagull*

I was at a river doing my morning practice of movement and sound when I thought about a recent situation in my life and got the feeling that I was scared of actually succeeding. Through

EXERCISE

Air, the messenger

This practice helps you to understand that all your goals and visions come through in divine timing. It will help you listen to the spirit of the wind as it holds the wisdom of the ether. Let yourself be carried on wings of devotion and effortlessness.

» Sit outside in the wind. Wear light clothing so that you can feel the wind on your skin. Come into a meditative state. Observe your breath inhaling and exhaling, making it long and deep for about five minutes. Then change your breath rhythm to be shallow, light and slightly accelerated for a few minutes.

» Invite a vision to come to you, focusing on your heart energy. Don't pay attention to what your breath is doing; let it do what it wants to do. Trust the form of vision you receive, a message, an image, a symbol, a memory, or anything else.

» Imagine the vision expanding and growing. Let it have wings to fly by focusing on the wind element. Witness what happens; let the air of imagination guide you. Trust what you sense and further receive.

» When you are ready to finish, bring your awareness back your breath, and practise slow deep breathing for a while.

» Journal and draw the experience to integrate. *Enjoy!*

sounding I saw that I needed to forgive myself and trust my word and my timing and receive the learning that is there for all. I stood in the river and connected with her flow, bathing my hands and blessing myself, as I allowed my grief to pour out through my voice. I had my eyes closed and when I opened them I had the sense that the land was moving and the river was still. That has become a powerful concept for me: *being still like a river and flowing with the movement of the earth*, as I yield to the flow of timelessness.

I then focused on the sun and imagined its flames all around me and in me. I let these flames build in my centre, as I sounded in forgiveness for an old fear of speaking the truth; for betrayal and for believing I was to blame or that I had to blame someone. I felt the flames transform me and burn my skin, and my eyes to burn out the old vision. I felt power and also humility in the presence of the sun and such vast potential.

I listened into the space around me, the stillness was intense and the sky was cloudless and brilliant. I closed my eyes and began sounding to the birds. Soon a pair of paradise ducks came and with their cries I felt a great freedom, which I sounded into my solar plexus and out to connect with Paradise — the ultimate forgiveness.

Finally I went into the earth and connected with my belief in myself and my gratitude to the Mother. I began to sound *I trust my power to succeed*. I cried and opened my heart to the heavens and let my feet sink into the earth. I felt I was received and that I received myself, grounded and whole. I felt new with a great sense of peace, forgiveness and gratitude. I completed my ritual by sounding my deepest love to Gaia for supporting me and giving me the space to grow.   ~ **Althea Lambert**

Sound healing to the elements

This is an advanced exercise; embark on it when you feel ready. I invite you to let all your compassionate healing frequencies reverberate and resonate throughout your being and to voice them to the planet. Practise on your own or with a group of like-minded people. We are one and we can play a significant role in healing Planet Earth. The responsibility begins with *you*. You will be rewarded a thousandfold. This practice is also profoundly self-healing.

» Call in the spirits of the earth, water, fire and air. Praise, acknowledge and sound their presence in the purest form as you create a strong picture of the elements being completely cleansed, purified and revitalised.

» Sound one element at a time or create an 'elemental synergy symphony'. Let the sounding grow step by step in intensity.

» When the sound healing is at its peak, visualise the sound frequencies travelling out into the earth itself, to the water, fire and air that are heavily polluted, stagnant or destroyed.

» You may be in contact with a specific element or several elements at the same time. Trust your intuitive visual perception. Trust that you will be guided to travel to specific areas of Planet Earth.

» Let your sound frequencies penetrate like laser beams with the intention of transforming for the greatest good of all and for the highest healing.

» Focus your attention so that you can be an effective, compassionate catalyst.

» A natural ending will emerge when the elements have truly received the sounds. Listen to the harmonious sounding and the cosmic intelligence of all things. Have faith that it has all been received with gratitude.

» Receive insights and messages in silence. Slowly come back by contacting your physical body and acknowledging your own sound healing power and wisdom.

» Honour that you *do* make a difference. *Enjoy!*

When you are in doubt,
be still, and wait.
When doubt no longer exists for you,
then go forward with courage.
So long as mists envelop you, be still.
Be still until the sunlight pours through and
dispels the mists — as it surely will.
Then act with courage.

PONCA CHIEF WHITE EAGLE

CHAPTER 11

Relaxation & surrender

The hidden power is surrender.
Be empty that the infinite can flow through you.
Be in the present moment,
make yourself ready for the unknown
in sweet surrender,
in trust.

I wake from a dream state and for a moment let dream and reality be one. I yearn to be in this state of surrender, the ecstatic response to full presence both in physicality and in spirit at the same time. The dream has shown me the complete safety of extending the present moment, letting the divine universe carry me in outstretched arms, which ultimately only my willingness to surrender can manage to embody.

I experience an all-embracing blanket of surrender that is teaching me to give up struggle, to let go of any expectations, concerns, doubts and tensions. Suddenly I am fully awake, with the distinct certainty that I am never alone. My guidance is whispering 'sweet surrender', and from this extended awareness *I am*.

> Our essential nature needs nothing at all from external means,
> but uses its internal landscape as the means to grow, and expand,
> and ultimately sit within a deep peace.   ~ **Gwyn Williams**

Let go of stress, and surrender

Surrender is a state of empowerment as we stop holding on to anything that is no longer important to us. When we stop forcing our will, we start to let the Now guide us, becoming aware of the whole. We agree to bend and we yield so as not to create tension and stress. We become as flexible as a tree in the wind. We flow with what is happening and what is inevitable.

It becomes a question of what we are willing to let go of to move more effortlessly and gracefully through life. Is it stress itself we are afraid of confronting or looking deeper into, or is it our attitude to our endeavours and our goal-oriented routines? It is not about what we are putting our hands and hearts into, but how we are doing it. It is not about a certain technique, but how we apply it.

I watch a dance performance where every cell in my body responds to the fluidity of talented, disciplined dancers moving in such organic rhythms and cycles. I am mesmerised and at the same time I feel hallowed and filled with a crystal-clear mystical energy in sweet surrender.

I am at a Leonard Cohen concert, falling into the deep space of a trance state. His inestimable musical capacity, even though he is in his mid-70s, moves a full-house audience to tears, as we all experience what it truly means to be an authentic singer and performer. An ecstatic, memorable experience.

The art of arts is relaxation. If we are able to move into a state of relaxation at any given moment, we are able to live in balance. As we stop resisting and reacting we smooth the hard edges and let go of being forceful. We use our strength in a gentle and firm way. We allow our yin and yang energy to be refined at still deeper levels, so the magical synchronicity between the two can manifest in our actions and being.

I recently had an experience at the dentist where my utmost faith in relaxation was required. A complex operation was needed on one of my teeth and the dentist explained it was not possible to do the procedure without local anaesthesia. I went along with this, but as the injection went in my whole body resisted, even though I was practising relaxation and deep breathing. My inner voice told me *this is not right for you*, and I fainted. At the next consultation I said no to the drug. The dentist looked at me as if I was weird and explained that he had never done this kind of operation without anaesthesia.

> *Stop sabotaging your potential. Slow down and cultivate a positive attitude in all matters.*

The journey was not so painful. I discovered that the pain was relative to my ability to stay absolutely present in a deeply accepting, relaxed state, as well as intently keeping my focus on breath, inner sounds and a yielding, flowing energy of trust. The dentist's remark after the operation was: 'You are truly unique!' After we had talked about my practice, he agreed that 'faith does move mountains.'

Consider how many people numb themselves with drugs and painkillers to ease physical, emotional or mental discomfort. The body is an instrument of wisdom and surrender that knows intuitively how to move pain and discomfort.

We become stressed because we want to be better, or different from what is right for us. We run away from a natural pace and rhythm and we forget to relax, to just stop and simply focus on our breath, for example. Some people are so stressed that when they finally go on holiday, they become sick. The overburdened, tensed body needs another kind of break. Sickness is the body's natural way of saying *Stop, no more*. Obey this and do not fight against it.

If stress becomes a habit, you are living on adrenaline. This is indicative of a belief system that says, 'If I stop, my world will fall apart'. However, it is safe to relax and experience chaos. It is safe to let your world fall apart for a moment, or for some days or maybe longer. It is safe to slow down, have some play time and set clear, healthy boundaries. It is safe to express your worries and concerns — you will still be loved. It is safe to say no, and trust the outcome of boundary setting. Reconsider your goals by taking good care of yourself always.

Check in with your breath and tone of voice to determine your stress level during the day; you may be surprised at what you discover. The first key to releasing stress is, *slow down*. Start to think of your stress as a friend and accept it. It is your responsibility to detect stress, to stop, to become conscious and to slow down. Stress arises when we disconnect, when we separate head and body, when we are not grounded or in contact with our body wisdom and inner listening.

EXERCISE

The regenerating sound and movement

This relaxation exercise help you to move and express with a minimum of effort. It is highly rejuvenating and can be done at any time. It gives you a sense of being completely rested, peaceful and in harmony with all that is.

>> Lie down on the floor and relax into your body, paying attention to your breath. You are now going to move your body and express sounds with no effort. When you are ready start a small movement and sound. It may be the tiniest motion and the smallest sound.

>> Don't control the sound and movement. Let the universe move and sound you from the core of your being, from where all action flows. You are being moved and sounded; you are not doing it. The dance of your body will come into a state of deepening relaxation and you will experience embodied beingness and effortlessness.

>> 'Let go and let God.' There is no question about where to go, no aim but being moved by the divine force. Allow yourself to yawn a lot, as this is a reflex of complete relaxation. Stay with the movement and sounding, as you are learning to be relaxed when in motion and expression.

>> When you have done this practice for 20 minutes or more you may feel like you have had a couple of hours of deep sleep.

>> Journal or draw the experience to integrate it before you slowly come back to your activity. *Enjoy!*

Doing is being and being is doing

Relaxation requires being able to detach. Detach yourself from being overly involved with too many things in life. Be who you are, instead of having to force or demonstrate your greatness. Be at peace with your smallness as well as your bigness. Allow ease and fun to be part of your life. Allow life to come to you instead of pushing against the river, forcing yourself to reach a goal or a destination. In a state of beingness you will acknowledge your receptivity in new and unexpected ways.

When you notice a sign of stress that has formerly been unconscious, begin to correct this habit in your daily activities. Are you breathing deeply or is your breath shallow? Are your stomach muscles tense? Is your mind busy or peaceful? When you move around, what is your usual way of walking? Are you swaying your hips or are they stiff? Are your shoulders relaxed so your head can move freely? Are your eyes relaxed when you read this book? *Surrender* is the magic word.

The eternal juggling and struggling between being and doing is related to our mastery of relaxation and surrender

When we move through life with ease and grace in a relaxed state and with a surrendering attitude, we experience life as coming towards us. And so it is with the phenomenon we call time. Time is coming towards us and not running away from us. True creation cannot reach us if we are tense, stressed or running away from the abundance that time itself gives us; living in a timeless consciousness is a great virtue to cultivate. We laugh more when we are relaxed and don't take ourselves so seriously. We may be so absorbed in living fully that there is no room for being stuck, or slaves to our habits. Life itself is constantly dancing us, as there is no change without movement. Take action to move any laziness — it takes

EXERCISE
Death meditation

One of the most effective relaxation exercises I know I call 'death meditation'. Allow yourself to reach the ultimate letting-go stage in a conscious way. The exercises may give you a floating sensation or an out-of-body experience. It is a safe relaxation and easy to practise. It gives you a strong sense of rejuvenation.

» Lie comfortably on the floor or on your bed; close your eyes, perhaps with eye shades covering them. Sink into deep relaxation by briefly asking your body to relax completely, offering reassurance that there is nothing to do or to think about. This is a sacred time for rejuvenation and wellbeing.

» Now contact your feet and ask them to relax. You may talk to them and say, for example, 'I love you, you can relax now, let yourself fall, expand and let go even more.' Sink even deeper into your feet, a sensation of falling and expanding. As you let go more and more you may feel the sensation of dropping through multiple layers. If you have any resistance, return to observe your breath and let the ease of your breath melt any fear or doubts.

» Here is the order of the areas you will be contacting. For each, do what is described above. The whole exercise may last 20–30 minutes.

- Feet
- Top of shoulders
- Heart
- Palm of the hands
- Tummy
- Eyes
- Neck
- Tailbone (coccyx)
- Feet

» When you return to the feet after the complete relaxation has finished, start to bring yourself back to the present moment by moving your feet and, when you are ready, gently start to stretch and move your entire body before opening your eyes.

» Listen to any insights by being completely still for an extended time. Trust what you sense and make your journal entry. *Enjoy!*

motion to stretch our limits and become alive. Go to the limit, then surrender. Be a warrior, dare to stumble and fall. The light is on our side.

Intimacy is life at its best. Take initiative for intimacy with your children, your partner, your friends and your loved ones, and create space for intimacy with yourself. Allow yourself to come closer and be seen; allow yourself to relax and surrender into being received.

In intimacy we fall into a place of surrender, of wonder, a feeling of coming home. Relaxation opens the gateway to authentic communication, the inner voice and the healing voice.

The five Tibetan rites

For more than two decades I have been practising a yoga called the five Tibetan rites. These are a series of ancient, dynamic yoga practices originally passed on to the Western world from a monastery in Tibet called the Fountain of Youth. Highly rejuvenating and relaxing, they balance the chakras and support detoxification of the system. (If you suffer from any severe conditions, contact a health practitioner before doing these practices regularly.)

If I miss my daily practice of the five Tibetan rites, I feel it. I have been experimenting with combining vowel sounds with these sacred rites and it works beautifully. Consciously moving with the designated vowel sound makes the exercises even more

EXERCISE
The intuitive flow of sound and movement

This practice uses movement and sound for intuition and creative expression, and develops joy and creative impulses so that they may be your guide.

>> Your dance floor could be anywhere — be creative. Set your body in motion with any movement, stretching, yoga, martial art or dancing. Now move in slow motion as you become more conscious of the movement.

>> When you feel at ease and relaxed in these improvised movements, watch your toes for a moment. Make an effort to separate your toes from one another, so they individually touch the ground. This creates a much stronger connection with the earth.

>> When you are ready, add sounds to your movement. The sound can be of any character; the more you practise spontaneity, the easier you match the movement in a non-controlled way. Look at the sound as an extension of your movement, and surprise yourself!

>> For each movement there is a sound expression and for each sound there is a movement expression. Move with certainty and pay conscious attention occasionally to your feet as you allow the earth to support you. Any time you feel insecure, come back to focusing on your toes.

>> Continue to move and sound in your own unique creation. Give yourself space and time. Let the exercise bring you satisfaction and effortlessness, and surrender to the flow.

>> When complete, listen to any insights, by being completely still for an extended time. Trust what you sense and make your journal entry. *Enjoy!*

fulfilling and uplifting. The following list of vowels is influenced by Maori and Hawai'ian language and culture, combined with my own understanding and experiences.

Description of vowels

AH (as in **far**) expresses foundation and grounding, spirit in matter, cleansing the physical, and gives a sense of satisfaction.

EH (as in **bet**) gets things moving and empowers; relates to life and all things.

EE (as in **bee**) speaks of directness and divine intelligence, time-balancing and mental clearing.

OH (as in **bore**) relates to roundness, innocence, peace, curiosity, and embracing eternity.

OO (as in **boom**) is uplifting and speaks of the communication and synchronicity of divine will, opening up our pure channel. (Hu is an ancient name for God).

The rites are completed twenty-one times each. If you are not familiar with this practice, I recommend starting out by doing the Five Tibetan Rites five times only. From there, increase according to your ability. Breathe through the nose on the inhaling breath and sound on the exhaling breath. Some may vary slightly from the original rites.

To each rite you may include an affirmation, which is related to the movement and the vowel sound. Each rite also relates to a chakra. Focus on the chakra and state the affirmation aloud before you start the rite. Repeat several times during the practice. Then focus on the breath, movement and sound.

Drop to the depths.
Dance on the edge.
Play till you fall.
Laugh till you cry.
Only then will you sing and soar
with your eagle's wings.

The five Tibetan rites

ONE

Spin clockwise with your arms outstretched. Keep your eyes focused on one point in your environment. After each spin, focus on the point. This will help prevent dizziness. If you do get dizzy, place your palms on the top of your shoulders and cross your arms in front of you. Sound on the vowel *ah* (for grounding and cleansing). Take a conscious, deep inhaling breath, followed by a smooth and long exhaling sound. Open your mouth wide on the *ah*-sound. For each spin, inhale and exhale, or inhale and exhale on alternate spins.

Affirmation: I am grounded and I am safe.
Chakra: Root

TWO

Lie on your back, palms towards the floor by your sides. As you inhale, lift your legs to a vertical position at the same time as you raise your chin towards your chest. On the exhaling breath, lower your outstretched legs slowly to the floor. Keep your chin relaxed as you sound on the vowel *eh* (for flow and empowerment). Take deep and slow breaths and let the sound fluctuate naturally on different pitches as you let go and open up to a sense of release. The slower you are able to do the exhaling sound and movement, the stronger the effect.

Affirmation: I am in the flow of life.
Chakra: Hara

THREE

Kneeling with your body upright, place your hands beneath your buttocks. Move your chin towards your chest in a forward motion, allowing the upper part of your chest to bend slightly as well. From there, take a deep inhaling breath as you arch the spine and lean backwards, stretching as far as you can. On the exhaling breath move from the backward arching position to the forward bending position, as you sound on the vowel *ee* (for directness and mental clearing). I recommend that on the inhaling breath you open your mouth wide as you stretch backwards, to avoid straining your throat.

Affirmation: I own my inner power.
Chakra: Solar plexus

FOUR

Sit on the floor with your legs stretched out and your arms along the side of your body, palms towards the floor. On an inhaling breath, arch your back as you lift yourself to a bridge-like position, arms straight, feet apart and knees bent, head leaning backwards. On exhaling, release the position and slowly move back to a sitting position with legs straight on the floor. Sound on the vowel *oh* (for innocence and peace) as you do this. Breathe deeply with long inhales and sounding exhales. Eventually allow the sound to fluctuate on different pitches.

Affirmation: I am interconnected with all that is.
Chakra: Heart

FIVE

Support your body in a crouching position, arching your back, with your arms outstretched and supporting your weight, the palms of your hands flat on the floor and your toes curled under. On an inhaling breath lift your body up to a Λ, bending at the hips, and putting your feet flat on the floor if possible. On exhaling, slowly move back to the starting position as described above, sounding the vowel *oo* (for uplifting and divine communication). If you feel any restriction in uttering the *oo*, let the sound develop into a wide open *ah*.

Affirmation: I am an open, clear and pure channel.
Chakra: Throat

CHAPTER 12

A world of compassion and oneness

*Compassion is the ultimate and most meaningful embodiment of emotional maturity.
It is through compassion that a person achieves the highest peak and deepest reach in their search for self-fulfillment.*
~ Jersild

His Holiness the Dalai Lama explains the meaning of compassion thus:

> Genuine compassion is based not on our own projections and expectations, but rather on the rights of the other: irrespective of whether another person is a close friend or an enemy, as long as that person wishes for peace and happiness and wishes to overcome suffering, then on that basis we develop a genuine concern for his or her problems. This is genuine compassion. Usually when we are concerned about a close friend, we call this compassion. This is not compassion; it is attachment. Marriages that last only a short time do so because of a lack of compassion; there is only emotional attachment based on projection and expectation. When the only bond between close friends is attachment, then even a minor issue may cause one's projections to change. As soon as our projections change, the attachment disappears, because that attachment was based solely on projection and expectation.

Compassion is the glue

Compassion is the glue that holds the world together, and it can truly change the world. Compassion is the emotion beyond all emotions, a quality so high in its essence that it allows an emotionally finely tuned person to be of the greatest service to humanity.

How do we respond to the suffering, misery and pollution of the world? With fear and judgment, or with compassion? How do we respond if somebody projects anger or frustration towards us? With reactions of rage or apathy, or with compassion? How do we respond when we are told we have made a mistake or should have done differently or better? With resentment and denial, or with compassion? In these fast-changing times we humans are being asked to go deeper within, because our planet is needing more compassion than ever before. Compassion is not just for the enlightened. *Compassion is for everyone to practise, so that we live in harmony and respect for one another and create peace on earth.*

I am in an overcrowded subway and can hardly breathe. From my survival instinct I begin to send compassion to the crowd,

and I focus on inner sounding. The freedom and sense of space is immediate.

I was on my way to visit a dear friend who had broken her wrist in an accident. She was experiencing excruciating pain, but she wished not to take painkillers during the doctor's manipulation of the bones. I sensed deep compassion for her as I sat by her side, sounding for an extended time. The easing of her pain was truly remarkable. Before I left she was able to continue the sounding process on her own and to monitor the pain, embodying self-compassion.

When I lecture and demonstrate at a conference I send compassion to the imaginary audience before they even arrive, and of course also during my presentation. The audience becomes much more receptive by being bathed and embraced in genuine compassion.

Compassion makes our service to humanity worthwhile. It teaches us to take care of our unreleased and suppressed emotional body. If you are filled with suppressed grief, anger or jealousy, how can you show true compassion?

Compassion is a wake-up call, and to take responsibility requires more than a caring heart. When you show somebody compassion you witness what holds them back and suppresses their soul's calling. When you are filled with compassion you support the person in a caring way with clarity and determination, according to what you *know* they need and not necessarily what they *think* they need. In other words, true compassion is when you yourself, freed from your own emotional attachments, are able to give support to another in their personal growth process. This is not always an easy task, to differentiate when a person is hiding or wanting attention to boost their ego or feed their self-pity. You may experience a person who is craving attention, complaining that 'Nobody helps me and I am all alone'. As long as the suffering person is not able to own their emotional shadows, there is nothing a compassionate person can actually do. Some people use sophisticated manipulation and power games to get what they want, but they may be lucky enough to meet a truly compassionate person who will show them that these strategies are not the way forward.

Nobody can move your emotional pains but yourself, and they cannot be removed by surgical operation. Don't wait for somebody to deliver you the 'Lotto win'.

Some people attract an illness so they can feel they are cared for and loved. You can only truly be supported if you are willing to look at your own suppressed emotions or unconscious projections.

Lord, make me an instrument of thy peace:
where there is hatred ... let me sow love
where there is injury ... pardon
where there is discord ... harmony
where there is doubt ... faith
where there is error ... truth
where there is despair ... hope
where there is sadness ... joy
where there is darkness ... light.
It is in giving, that we receive.
It is in pardoning, that we are pardoned.
It is in dying (into ourselves), that we are
born to eternal life.
ST FRANCIS OF ASSISI

Kristin Flood, author of a compelling book about St Francis of Assisi, says: 'The first wealth is about becoming big; the second one about becoming small.'

> I was facilitating a sound session with a client who had experienced deep trauma in her childhood. As I was sounding into her solar plexus I sensed a subtle, yet solid sensation coming through me, as my physical body became very hot. I sensed Mother Mary strongly and felt deep and sacred compassion for the client. This was also reflected in my sounds. My sounds then changed as they connected to the fear and grief within the client. She instantly started to squirm and spontaneously cried out, stating she had severe pain in her back which felt like hot knives cutting through her. I used body touch and encouraged her to trust this process by reassuring her she was safe. She screamed out sounds of rawness that were coming from deep within her until she was empty of this emotional pain. Because my client was willing and felt safe to express her own sounds, spontaneous healing was instant and transformative for her.
>
> The client said she felt my sounds were penetrating her and opening her up to feel the intense waves of grief and fear moving through her; waves which she felt safe to ride as she released through her own sounds. As this settled she experienced waves of light and a divine feminine presence with her.
>
> My Soul Voice training is helping me to clear and heal at deep levels; it enables me to connect to a greater spiritual Presence in my life, and to feel worthy to embody this presence within me.
>
> ~ **Jenny Glover**

I am teaching my students to teach compassion, to take self-responsibility and to find their true answers from within. Compassion comes from a heart that is living in surrender, in prayer and in devotion to be of the highest service and clearest channel.

Imagine compassion being introduced to hospitals or to our politicians, ghettos, prisons and war zones; how would that change the world?

Consider that it all starts with *you*, and that you can do it. *Even if your faith is only as big as a mustard-seed, you can move mountains now.*

➡ **TRY THIS:** Show compassion by letting an elder who is in the queue behind you go in front of you.

» Slow down and show compassion to the cashier when you go shopping.
» Be patient and have compassion with yourself when you make mistakes or cannot meet deadlines.
» Show compassion by giving a donation to an organisation that supports the highest good for the planet.
» Show compassion to those you may consider your enemies, those who trigger you and make you feel inadequate.

You will thus transform yourself and the world.

≈

I sit in meditation and give thanks to all those who have gone before me, and those I feel connected to in my life. The ancestors in my own lineage, my father and mother who showed me exceptional compassion and trust by allowing me to be a free spirit. To the others of my lineage who worked with and cultivated the earth with such respect and dignity. I give thanks to my spiritual ancestors who showed me the shamanic way, leading me to the medicine of my soul's passion, the voice.

I give thanks to all my beautiful and powerful students, practitioners and teachers who are committed to spread the Soul Voice work to the world and who make such a grand difference with their compassionate contributions.

Compassion follows gratitude. When we praise and give thanks for what abundance we have, it will multiply and come back to us. We become a magnet of attraction when our heart is overflowing with compassion and gratitude.

Dr Wayne Dyer says in his book, *The Power of Intention*:

> Being in a state of gratitude is the exact same thing as being in a state of respect — respect for yourself, which you give away freely, and which will return to you tenfold. Jesus of Nazareth spoke through his apostle St Matthew (Matthew 5:48): 'Be perfect, therefore, as your heavenly Father is perfect'. Reconnect to the perfection from which you originated. You can't have any more self-respect than that!

Compassion fosters oneness

When we live in compassion, oneness will follow. Oneness is a state of being where we feel connected to all that is, no matter what happens. It is a state of pure knowingness that we will never be alone. It is a place within, from which our breath and life force originate, a surrendering place of eternal movement and devotion. Oneness is peace originating from our divine presence of heart. Oneness is a knowingness that the planet cannot die, nor can the soul. We create peace and oneness by clearing any unresolved issues or communicating what we may need to communicate to another person.

EXERCISE
Gratitude multiplies

This practice opens the portals to genuine thankfulness. Gratitude creates a magnet for abundance to flow into your life. Practising gratitude creates unexpected miracles.

» Have pen and paper available and sit in a quiet place. Ask your compassionate heart who you are to write a letter of gratitude to? Take one person at a time, and one piece of paper for each person.

» As you start writing, practise 'automatic intuitive writing', which means do not lift the pen from the paper to reflect. You are to write continuously with no breaks. Even if you have nothing to say, simply write that. This is a technique for engaging your right hemisphere, your intuitive brain, which allows greater spontaneity and intuition to flow through you.

» Focus on the gratitude aspect of the writing and use lots of I-statements, which will make the letters personal and engaging. Trust the process and be aware of your breath. Write as many letters as you desire in one round.

» When completed, sit in silence and meditate with gratitude in your heart. Smile and sense the effect gratitude has.

» When you are ready, take a walk to integrate the process and read the letters aloud to the nature spirits. This process can be a great revelation in itself, as nature listens unconditionally to you and acts as a mirror.

» Keep your gratitude letters as long as they have importance for you. Then burn them with a prayer, honouring the transformation that fire brings. Bury the ashes or scatter them in a stream.

» Listen for completion. Eventually draw the experience. *Enjoy!*

A journal entry from the time of my mother's death transition:

When my mum passed over I experienced a new kind of oneness. My mum had lost her power of speech several years prior to her death, which made her quite vulnerable and intuitive in a remarkable way. Subsequently I had many profound eye-gazing experiences with her. It enabled me to be in a grander feeling space and intimacy with her and with myself, which often seemed to be from another plane and dimension, an experience that I do not have many words for. It was as if a veil had lifted and we were one.

I arrived 24 hours after she had passed over, but she was still present in spirit with the most innocent, beautiful and compassionate face that I have ever seen on her. She had been hyperventilating for three days and nights without interruption; what a life-force! I felt Mother Mary's presence strongly. My mum was already one with spirit, although present with me in an angelic form. During that night she came to me and said with a clear voice in Danish, 'I feel so good and grateful and I feel safe.'

For what is it to die
but to stand naked in the wind
and to melt into the sun?
And what is it to cease breathing,
but to free the breath
from its restless tides,
that it may rise and expand
and seek God unencumbered?
Only when you drink
from the river of silence
shall you indeed sing.
And when you have reached
the mountain top,
then you shall begin to climb.
And when the earth
shall claim your limbs,
then shall you truly dance.
KAHLIL GIBRAN, *THE PROPHET*

Quan Yin,
ascended master of
compassion says,
'I will not leave Planet Earth
before every human being is
living in happiness.'
What a compassionate
statement!
Watch out,
she is still around,
and maybe she is
a part of YOU.

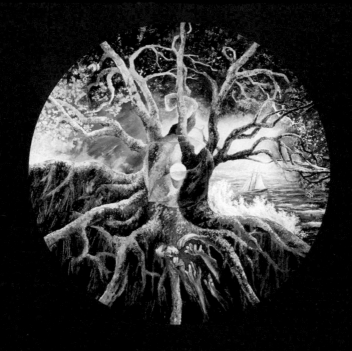

CHAPTER 13

Telepathic planetary sound healing & the Soul Voice community

The Calling is present
as never before —
the Calling to be heard through
your own uniqueness and vibration.
Together we can move mountains.
The seed is planted
by YOU taking action.
The Calling is to practise
the commitment it takes to
make a difference.
Peace and compassion on earth now.

Resonate the
Calling from the heart.
Be filled and be fulfilled
with the collective support.
Stand tall and humble to speak
the forgotten tongue, the language
of all nations, the voice that unites,
the truth of all things.
The Calling is YOU.
Express your destiny in
remembrance, to freedom.

A message from a Hopi elder:

> There is a river flowing now
> very fast. It is so great and swift that there
> are those who will be afraid. They will
> try to hold on to the shore. They will
> feel they are being torn apart and suffer
> greatly. Know the river has its destination.
> The elders say we must let go of the shore,
> push off into the middle of the river, keep our
> eyes open, and our heads above the water. And
> I say, see who is in there with you and celebrate! At this
> time of history we are to take nothing personally, least
> of all ourselves. For the moment that we do, our spiritual
> growth and journey comes to a halt. The time of the
> lone wolf is over: Gather yourselves! Banish the word
> 'struggle' from your attitude and vocabulary. All that we
> do now must be done in a sacred manner and in celebration. We
> are the ones we've been waiting for.
>
> ~ Oraibi, Arizona Hopi Nation

Global awareness and collective consciousness

The ripples that radiate out from a stone thrown into a pond can metaphorically represent our sense of ever-widening identity. 'Whenever two or more are gathered, I am among you,' Jesus said. How do we significantly heighten consciousness and evolution through collective effort and joint intentions? What are the forces behind our spirituality that allow us to go so much faster and deeper into our personal growth process, when the collective consciousness has one focus?

> I recently experienced a traumatic miscarriage. I felt alone, miserable, and that I had done something wrong. With a gentle nudge from Karina and some reluctance, I told my Global Sound Tribe what had happened. (The Tribe consists of certified practitioners around the world who I have not met.) I was overwhelmed with messages of love and offers of sound sessions. Some met face to face to sound to me as a group. Others sent their sound through

the ether at various times, but during the two weeks that followed my loss, I was constantly receiving sound from somewhere in the world. I felt the overlap of different practitioners sounding and what I imagine a tuning fork would feel if constantly used. My physical body healed quickly as I allowed myself to receive this amazing gift. I have no doubt that the reason for my speedy recovery was the collective sound being sent. Old emotions and patterns of abandonment and loss resurfaced and healed. I became aware of, or rather remembered, that I am always fully loved and supported. This feeling of being supported is a new one for me and one that I am still integrating every day.

One project we have started as a Global Sound Tribe is to connect telepathically every month. We simultaneously sound to the elements according to the season, with the intention of healing that element not only outside us but also in our bodies. It is a powerful coming together of many voices as one. I have complete faith that what we are doing commands a great force of energetic healing that ripples through our world. With one powerful voice we have intensified and magnified our intention. This monthly connection is just a beginning, but all the same it has deepened my sense of who I am as an individual and awakened the sense of oneness and divinity. I have the knowledge that at our purest essence, we are all one — and more importantly, I feel it!

~ Melissa McCormack

Sounding collectively with intention and presence is an awakening experience, where the effect of each person's sounding is greatly multiplied. In a collective experience where voices merge into each other in a divine union, new frequencies and outcomes will occur.

The power and the impact of collective energy is huge. When we can follow our individual guidance, together perhaps with a mentor, we can experience mystical divine power and radically change the vibrations of our chosen goals.

I founded the Soul Voice method from an inner knowingness and guidance and a strong calling to create community. Our old ways of staying alone in our caves of hidden agendas, egos and greed, are coming to an end and need to be transformed to an altruistic attitude. This takes us to unknown places, to missing

links, to the forgotten mystery, to a connection on still deeper levels, where oneness and remembrance are our guides. To create a collective awareness with clear intent and commitment to ourself is a continuously deepening emotional, mental and spiritual cleansing process for the highest good of all.

Choosing commitment without attachment or expectation brings us to the present moment fully alive, so that we soar in the highest joy, in union and in devotion.

> I used to think of myself and my Soul Voice practice as an island. Of course there was a ferry that, once in a while, went to another island where another practitioner or teacher lived. But still we were islands connected by a ferry with a time schedule and we had to run the island alone. It wasn't until I got the experience of being a teacher that I slowly started to change. In the beginning as a Soul Voice teacher my loneliness and not being a part of the group became very visible. I worked very hard to show my students what a great teacher I was so I could be a part of the group. But of course that didn't work.
>
> At that time I was being coached by Karina in a delicate and deep way, which helped me to surrender these old mechanisms of separation. I dived deeply into the depths of old memories and

traumas, so they could heal. In return I got a new awareness of receiving support. I realized it has been there all the time, I was just too occupied with my own stuff to receive it.

We are all connected in a big sea of sound-waves. We cannot be separated. The Soul Voice community is a strong container and field, woven around the planet. I tap into this field whenever I need it and experience an enormous support. I believe that we are also globally invited to give up our islands of pain and separation and start remembering who we truly are. And when we do so and connect to the collective field, we can work miracles together, personal and planetary. We overcome time and place with our frequencies and penetrate deep into our core.

~ **Marinet Koeman**

I want to conclude this book with a chakra self-healing alignment, as well as a telepathic planetary sound healing to the chakras. (See further explanation on the chakras in Chapter 9).

As part of the Soul Voice teaching, I have created a sound healing practice to our planet's chakra system for the purpose of telepathic healing, so that we can extend the vision of creating balance and harmony in all kingdoms.

When we look at the earth intuitively there are distinct chakras not only for the whole globe, but indeed in each country. When I guide these collective sound healings I allow each participant to use their own intuitive abilities and clair-audiant skills to place the chakras where they are drawn to, in their country or on Planet Earth.

There are various theories about this subtle energy system, the chakra system, related to Planet Earth. As with the theory of specific ley lines and the grid system, some of the most common perceptions are as follows:

» Root chakra, Grand Canyon, Sedona and Mt Shasta, North America
» Hara chakra, Machu Picchu, Peru
» Solar Plexus chakra, Uluru, Australia
» Heart chakra, Glastonbury, UK, and the Ganges River, India
» Throat chakra, the Great Pyramid, Egypt
» Pineal chakra, Mt Fuji, Japan
» Crown chakra, Mt Kailash, Himalaya, Tibet

Remember that there are thousands of places on earth which are power-spots and vortices, so do not limit your perception.

Planetary telepathic sound healing

The following practice will lift you to a greater understanding of life, a strong sense of community and connectedness to humanity. It will expand your faith in healing the planet and give a sense of 'being as one'. As you give you shall receive and as you receive you shall give, a thousandfold.

» Set up a sacred space and come into a meditative body position. Be still and listen. Let the *AUM* sounding permeate from the root to the crown chakras as you focus on your inner centre-line by visualising an empty 'bamboo shoot'. Let the *A* resonate in the root, continue along the centreline to the heart-throat area on the *U* and finish at the pineal-crown on the *M* humming sound. Do the *AUM* sounding as long as is needed for centring and 'in-tuning'.

» Call in the highest healing for the elements, your country and Planet Earth. Stay in compassion and focused intention to the best of your ability.

» Contact the root chakra area through deep breathing of the colour red. Visualise the qualities of safety and groundedness as you bring them into your root chakra, and match with sound frequencies.

» After a couple of minutes of sound healing, be still. Let the silence support the self-healing.

» Now, focus your root chakra frequencies at a distance of two to three metres in front of you. Visualise a violet-coloured crystal bowl. Let the frequencies gather in the bowl. Sound heal with the intention of the highest healing for

the root chakra of your country or the planet. Trust, even if you do not yet have a clear picture of the chakra location on earth.

» After a couple of minutes of sound healing, allow in silence the frequencies of the 'gathered' root chakra energy to travel on sound waves to its destination. Simply be present and let it happen. Trust your intuition and visualisation and have faith in the guidance and any images you may receive in this telepathic process. Aim to let the frequencies permeate, harmonise and awaken higher consciousness.

» When the process feels complete, start to return to physical presence; come back to here and now. Proceed to the next chakra with its corresponding colour and qualities and repeat the above. The chakras' colours and qualities are as follow:

 – **Hara chakra:** orange; the qualities of flow, flexibility, play and pleasure.
 – **Solar plexus chakra:** yellow; the qualities of inner power, passion, boundary setting and directness.
 – **Heart chakra:** green; the qualities of compassion, love, self-nurturing and interconnectedness.

- **Throat chakra:** light blue or turquoise; the qualities of freeing expression, clear communication, freedom and truth.
- **Pineal chakra:** indigo blue; the qualities of understanding, clarity of mind and consciousness.
- **Crown chakra:** violet; the qualities of devotion, oneness, faith and divine meaning.

» To close this profound experience gently and slowly, contact the chakras in your own body, starting with the crown chakra and finishing at the root chakra. Sense your physical body and your energy body being bathed in the seven rainbow colours in the highest frequencies and qualities. Give thanks to the sound healing that took place for your country's or planet's chakra system.

» Stay in total faith and trust that the frequencies were received and the highest healing performed.

» When complete, relax by lying on the ground in silence. Journal the experience when you are ready. Take a walk to integrate it.

» If you are in a group setting, let everyone share their experience with a buddy or collectively. *Enjoy!*

The earth's pulse and rhythm are calling us. The songs and the song lines are calling us loudly, to contribute to the harmony of all things, to respect all kingdoms, to use all our power, wisdom, love and telepathic abilities for the highest healing. We all have these. Sound frequencies can travel wherever there is an intention of purpose and compassion. Have faith. Open yourself and listen to where in your country or on the planet, your attention goes in this moment, in your willingness to support.

As you send your healing frequencies and positive intentions to the living earth you shall receive in return, in many unpredictable ways.

The following practice may be done with a group of people. Gathering with a like-minded group is uplifting and empowering. It is important to be focused, purposeful and compassionate. Create a group energy based on harmony and love, and honour your differences with loving kindness and understanding. You may also choose to do this practice on your own.

Note, when you send to the chakras of the planet, let yourself be guided intuitively about where they may be.

Carry your unique frequencies and authentic expression out to humanity and be brave in doing so. It takes courage and perseverance to make an important difference that our world is so in need of.

Spread what you have learnt in this book, so we can lift each other up to higher frequencies and live in balance, presence and authenticity in our daily lives. Let your light and expression shine, alone or together. Dare to be seen and be heard, as you will bring invaluable gifts to yourself and those you interact with.

As I watch the Pacific Ocean from our house, I hear the waves crashing towards the shore. Planet Earth and its inhabitants are living on an edge, facing big changes, which compel us to change from within, to let go and to surrender. Let us weave the web of ancient wisdom, sacredness and authentic expression and abundance, knowing that divine timing is this present moment.

As I dwell upon completing this book I feel a growing inner and outer support for my vision — in resonance, joy and freedom.

Allow yourself to be passionate, compassionate and committed to sound as you listen and express your destiny fully. Heal yourself, humanity and the world, and allow yourself to be heard in your new awakening resonance.

In sacred resonance
Karina Schelde
Coromandel New Zealand, June 2012

Case stories
from Soul Voice practitioners

Releasing fear

When Karina asked me to share a story of a client's experience with fear, I suddenly went blank. I jogged my memory and could not recall a single experience of a client moving through fear. I immediately understood that I had a pattern of fear in myself needed to address.

I went through a session to reacquaint myself with this emotion. I have done this many times before but realised I had fallen asleep to some of the deeper drives and callings of my soul. As I went through the layers of numbness, my breathing became rapid and irregular as the suppressed energy of fear was allowed to reveal itself. I truly embraced it and 'stared it straight in the eyes.'

The sounds that came out brought a stream of images, illuminating unprocessed thought patterns that were holding emotional charge. One in particular was a deep desire to get into surfing. My body loves the water and this feels like a wonderful pastime for me to enjoy in this lifetime. During my sounding process I felt fear of big waves and worry about not coping, about getting hurt — this had been stopping me from surfing. When I allowed myself to fully feel the fear, it transmuted into pure, raw, available energy. I felt highly energised and fully present.

The first time I went surfing after this I felt the butterflies in my stomach. I had to consciously feel into and embrace these sensations. I was able to change my internal atmosphere to one which welcomed the thrill of adventure.

Meanwhile I had been working regularly with a client with sound and watching him come deeper into his own sense of power and consequently making empowered decisions. One of these decisions was to begin playing rugby again in his mid-30s. We had been working on recognising the energy of fear by finding the exact sound that the fear felt like and watching it transform itself.

He had been selected to play A-grade rugby and this particular Saturday his team was playing against what he described as 'massive giants'. He later said that just before he went onto the field he felt an overwhelming fear of being hurt (not being fit enough, not strong enough, too old). He fully felt into it and it totally disappeared, leaving him feeling confident. As a consequence he had a very good, physical game.

This helped me realise how naturally we can guide someone into territory once they have adventured there themselves. I learned how effective sound can be in creating new energetic pathways to let us to go beyond our fears.

~ **Chad Beckett, Australia**

Emotional transformation

A challenging client, Raina, had an alcoholic and angry father. She was conceived by rape. She told me about childhood memories of threatening and violent scenes. After her parents divorced, Raina never saw her father again.

Following a couple of initial Soul Voice sessions I was sounding to her belly, when suddenly the sounds came out strongly, dramatically and primordially with lots of dissonance. I channelled through the sounds of the client's horrifying memories to achieve the greatest release and healing. It was a most powerful session.

Raina revealed in the debriefing afterwards that she was going to have surgery on her uterus soon because she was carrying a fibroid as big as a grapefruit!

The day after our session, she called me and told me: 'While the doctors were doing the ultrasound scan to prepare for surgery, they found no fibroids, and they even asked me if I was making a fool of them! I spent the whole night after the session with very strong contractions, almost more painful than those during labour. I actually saw that I was losing a lot of blood, but I did not care.'

She continued: 'After finishing our last session, I drove for the first time to my daddy's grave' — I had never heard her call him that — 'I thought it was time after ten years! And I wrote him a note in which I told him that I loved him. I left the message there on his grave next to a flower.'

~ Maura Chiara Letizia Montanari, Italy

Dying in peace

A nurse told me about a resident, Lucy, who the other nurses and family members were at a loss to help. She was in pain despite all her medications. Her skin was so fragile that it tore with any movement of her body. She was unconscious, restless, and moaned in discomfort. Everyone had expected her to die days before.

I entered Lucy's room slowly. Sitting beside her I asked for permission within to sound to support her highest wellbeing and got a 'yes'. Because of the state of her skin I was unable to touch her, so I allowed myself a few minutes to tune in energetically. I sensed blocks in her heart and crown chakras. Gently I sounded over her heart while listening within: I intently observed Lucy's face and body for responses. Within a few minutes her aura started to clear. I continued with tender yet soulful sounds that could touch into her depths and at the same time respect the delicate sensitivity of one on the threshold between worlds.

I paused and caught my breath. I'd been sounding for ten minutes. Her eyes were now open and clear. Her restlessness had decreased. Her moans were less frequent. I resumed a light but directed sounding for her crown. The sounds were high and full of love. I sounded for another seven minutes, after which I sensed it was time to stop.

I sat with Lucy for a while to remain in our co-created field and to be present with the grace and stillness that had blossomed around her. Lucy's eyes were shining, clear and open. The moans stopped and the restlessness was gone. I left with the sense that she would die shortly. The next morning Lucy took her last breath.

~ Valerie Moysey, Canada

Cellular memory reprogramming for teenagers

Francesca, 17 years old, is a young woman who is in strong conflict with her school and family, to such an extent that she decided to run away from home. I became the only person she was willing to discuss her issues with, so I got the authorisation from her parents to meet with her regularly. After some coaching meetings I was finally ready to give a sound session to her reproductive system. Working on her womb, I saw a very small fetus with its umbilical cord flying away among lots of blood. It became a very touching session. Francesca cried; she felt a huge pain and sadness in her entire body. She didn't understand what it was, just that she had experienced strong emotions that had left her weakened. We finished the session by honouring the healing that had taken place and lit a candle with a prayer.

After some days I had a phone conversation with Francesca's mother. Having shared my experience of Francesca's session, she revealed to me that she had had an abortion between the birth of the first daughter and Francesca. She had kept it as a secret until now.

It became obvious that Francesca had got the imprint from her mother of that guilt and shame, and that she was carrying the pain of the unborn baby in her cellular memory. Our session was the key to the unravelling process. The mother told Francesca about the abortion. This allowed Francesca to regain the relationship with her mother, to find a new place of peace within herself and to start a longer process to becoming closer to her father as well.

~ **Maria Christina Franzoni, Italy**

Healing the land with sound

I was attending a gathering of an ancient, peace-loving people of Aotearoa New Zealand. A large group of us walked onto the headland at the mouth of the great Hokianga Harbour. The elder women called us onto their sacred land with haunting cries.

Suddenly, I was gripped by an awful feeling. Below me, I saw a vision of a historic scene: many waka (war canoes) were in the harbour and a brutal battle was taking place. The waters ran red with blood. Slashed bodies lay on the shore and in the water. A few bodies were sucked out through the narrow harbour entrance into the open sea.

The people around me were laughing, chatting and enjoying the day as normal. My unease did not go away, nor did the strong vision of the scene. Shocked and angry at the intrusion, I tried to make it go away. Slowly, it came to me that it was happening for a reason and that somehow I was being called to it. I opened to my intuition and asked *What needs to happen here?* The word *acknowledgement* came. I began making terrible sounds of the warriors demanding recognition and honour for their war deeds of killing and bloodlust (things that I abhor).

After a time I connected to a universal love that was beyond the events happening before me. A love that encompasses all human potentials, beyond my personal opinions and judgments about peace and war. I carried on sounding and gradually the sounds became pure, universal sounds and the vision faded. It was as if allowing the warrior to be heard had somehow allowed it be transmuted to a higher form of expression.

This was not an easy or pleasant experience and yet it has shown me the truth of the bigger picture of universal love. I am eternally grateful to Karina and the Soul Voice training for giving me the tools to use in *any* situation!

~ Linda Duff, United Kingdom

Visualisation and intent

I was spending time in the mountains with my family when suddenly my son Mateo fell sick with a high temperature. I did not have any remedies with me so I had Mateo lie down next to me, comforting him before starting to sound. The sounds were like whispers that progressively turned into water energy. After a while the sensation became clearer, I visualised a mountain stream and gently sounded this visualisation. The energy of the river was flowing over my son, who immediately fell asleep. I remained with him, sounding softly, as the fever decreased. Then I left him sleeping for a while. When he woke up the fever was completely gone. It was a simple yet significant experience for me that taught me how visualisation, the elements and my pure intent can work together for the highest healing.

~ Viria Romagnoli, Italy

Moving beyond limits

I have been working with Sally, 72 years young, in a series of Soul Voice sessions. She has a history of overworking as a massage therapist and taking care of others at the expense of her own wellbeing. She is now retired on a disability pension.

In this particular session Sally connected with intense pain in her back. I supported her in staying present, sounding through the pain as it moved and finally cleared. Sally felt tired and gradually became quiet. Normally I would accept this and bring the session to a close, but I felt strongly that Sally was limiting herself in her tiredness. I gently invited her to feel the tiredness and sound it. I kept speaking and encouraging her quietly and gently with sounds, but her resistance continued. I asked her whether this was a way of limiting herself. Sally started to sound deeply into her belly and she laughed. Again I felt she was backing off and at the same time I intuited that another part of her wanted to keep on going. I asked her, 'Is this really enough for you?' and encouraged her to make the sound of it being really enough. Sally did take to it and then all of a sudden she just *totally* went for it. She started to sound and couldn't stop; she became the sound. I kept on coaching and supporting her. She shook her body wildly as she released the full range of tones in complete joy and freedom. Sally even started to find her own 'language'. At a certain point she was finally complete.

Transformed and in awe, she said, 'My life will never be the same again. I feel as though I touched my essence, being present with it all, even the pain in my back. I really get it now.'

Since then Sally has continued to live from a place of no limits. She left a restrictive relationship, and released other roles in her life in order to finally feel free to be herself. People now compliment her on her exuberance. Recently Sally supported her daughter birthing her fourth child by walking down the hospital corridors strongly chanting *Om!*

~ Cheryl Middleton, Australia

Positive reprogramming

I have been delighted to give sessions to my partner, who writes and sings his own songs and who wishes to become a professional musician. Four years ago he lost his wife and decided to stop singing to be able to care for his four children, and so continued with his regular work. I fell in love with him because of his songs and lyrics, so it was hard for me to see him make that decision.

He eventually started to doubt this decision, and as I was giving him an 'emotional release reprogramming' session one day I realised that he didn't allow himself to be supported by the universe; that he shut himself down from his true talent and higher self. It was so obvious that I almost had to hide my smile seeing him struggle for the answer that was right in front of him. When he came to a point of serene silence I suddenly heard him saying the words 'I am supported by God.' He then started sounding his positive programming for 21 days. Every day was a new revelation and he gained more and more confidence. He picked up his guitar again and started to write songs. He released a beautiful album and his new profession as a songwriter and musician now gives him a sustainable income. I am honoured to be his personal coach in this process.

~ Joyce Hellendoorn, The Netherlands

Telepathic sound healing

On Delphine's 37th birthday I initiated her with a Soul Voice session. Delphine felt a deep feeling of failure, of having no purpose in her life. She felt profoundly wounded in her heart. In addition, she recently experienced energetic invasion with a strong feeling of a breach in the whole pelvis area.

With telepathic sound healing through the ethers, I immediately felt a supportive and earthly feminine energy bringing confidence and safety through overtone sounds to Delphine's pelvic area — deep lower pitch, spinning slowly and regularly. I sensed roots coming out of her feet and grounding deep down into the earth. Then the sounds softened, opened, became a lullaby; the volume changed like waves and was like Mother Earth talking to Delphine, saying, *Come on, wake up, stand up! You are not alone, I support you!* As I continued to sound those comforting frequencies I sensed the breach being healed. I moved inwardly to her heart and received the image of a black thorn. I followed the sounds guided by the air element, combining tone, volume and rhythm. After a while I saw the thorn being gently lifted up in a bright light soundscape. Those sounds increased in pitch, getting higher and lighter, becoming like air. I intentionally sent subtle breath to the wound and it softly healed with every exhale, deeper and deeper. Finally I saw the heart radiate its own light in a regular pulse.

Later Delphine shared with me on the phone. After some time feeling her body gently vibrating, she heard a big sound within, as if someone had slammed a door. She felt a short shock, but thereafter she was able to receive vibrations resonating and shaking her whole body and being. She heard the last sounds as waves of peace. One week later, she was singing out in nature, feeling completely confident and joyful again.

~ **Murielle Reymond, USA**

Transformation through group collective support

As I have been through so many transformations during the Soul Voice practitioners' training, I was not expecting what happened to me as an assistant in a two-day Soul Voice workshop. I was ready to support others during their processes, but since the group had uneven numbers I was also going to be part of the process doing the exercises. I thought, *No problem, I know them all very well, it will be easy.* During the 'song of the soul' exercise I received a collective sound healing for the first time to both my first names, Rebekka Gabriela. As my third eye was balanced through the infinity symbol, I felt more complete than ever. But this was just a preparation for the next step, the 'clearing the clouds' meditation. I was never before able to let go so much at once. Exhausted and almost out of breath from shaking and moving my body, from shouting and screaming out all false pictures and judgments about how a woman should be, and how I should be, I started to sound the 'blue sky', the meditative stage.

What I call heaven then opened up for me. It was like standing on a high point somewhere in the universe, seeing the blue sky. Heaven was above me, behind me, underneath me, in front of me. It was huge and infinite. An angelic being appeared, inviting me to see more, and I became aware of receiving new guidance. Touched to tears, wide open, freezing and hot at the same time, I could hardly contain all the love and light that was present around and in me. Yes, this was a real initiation, another new chapter in my life. Knowing and practising all these wonderful healing techniques from the practitioners' training for so many months, I experienced how deep and effective even the simplest Soul Voice exercise can be — especially when supported by a strong collective group energy.

~ Rebekka Gabriela Specht, Switzerland

My power animals are my teachers

I walked my inner paths. I confronted challenges. I set myself the task to find my power animal, supported by my spirit guide. First I found the eagle on my path: My arms stretched, moved sinuously, rending the air to find resistance and support my flight. I looked at the world from above and saw things from a different perspective. The eagle is inside me; the beat of its heart sounds like a drum in my chest and we are as one. Its power remains, and has grown inside me, step by step. It gives me the essence of lightness, a connection with my soul, and the ability for my body to expand. The eagle's ability to fly high and alone in the sky is like a meditation: my cells vibrate in the sound of silence and can regenerate. To look from above changes my everyday perspective so I can now see and heal hidden emotions. The eagle is my travelling companion; it is always near me.

Later I experienced another power animal. This animal did not reveal itself as an image or a dream but it came to me when my mind was free from every thought and my heart clear of the forces which kept me imprisoned by old beliefs. At first I perceived the way it walked and the vibration that the earth was transmitting to me. Each of its steps was my step and I understood I belonged to it. The elephant had found me. My feet became enormous and heavy. I felt the energy of the earth sustaining me and encouraging me. My body became bigger and more round. The way I walked became firm and regal while my waving trunk was capturing the smells in the air. The generous elephant brought to me primordial memories of ancient lives, of the knowledge and power of medicine men, and made me aware of my capability to understand. I could go into the obscure zone of the unconscious and perceive the true emotional energy transmitted by sounds. I could let them into my body to perceive the pure essence of mortal beings. The elephant guided me in long unknown paths, in the passage between life and death without fear of death.

Today I have two allies. From them I can get incredible energy, psychically and mentally. At the same time I have to nourish them to maintain a strong relationship with them. In Italian the eagle is a female noun and the elephant is a male noun, so the animals also represent my female and male sides.

~ Marco Lugaresi, Italy

Sexual abuse release

Susan had severe abuse issues. She had distanced herself from real life and had a lack of self-worth. She had tried many healing methods, including going to psychologists, but still she felt severely out of balance. She was aware she needed to dive deeper, so she was ready for the Soul Voice method.

When I started to work with her, her contact with her feelings was sporadic and minimal. The initial sessions were mostly me as an active facilitator, which helped Susan gain confidence in herself and trust the healing effect of sounds. I taught her how to release pain from her body through expressing sounds herself. I then went through a series of sessions with her, utilising various Soul Voice sound healing techniques to come to the essence of her deep-rooted abuse issues.

Her life transformed radically on all levels. She learnt how to set healthy and clear boundaries, to accept her feelings and to deal with them. She learnt not to project her guilt and shame, to own it and to release it. Susan is now able to forgive herself and those involved in her former life of abuse and being a victim. She is a woman in her own power in touch with her intuition.

~ Ulla Maglekilde Jerrebo, Denmark

Sound and ancient remembrance

Amanda was a renowned professional singer and musician who played the flute like magic and had an angelic singing voice. I called her the Pied Piper as her youthful energy, enthusiasm and laughter — fused with song and flute — were contagious. Amanda suddenly became ill and tragically passed away only a week after being admitted to hospital with complications from a rare skin disease.

This was the first time someone close to me had died and it is difficult to describe the emotional turmoil which swept through my entire body. I had to release these deep emotions, this explosive energy that was devouring me. I was desperate to *sound it out loud.* Sounds poured through me. I sounded my intense sadness and grief, I sounded my absolute shock and disbelief, I sounded my raging anger and frustration, I sounded into the fear of my own mortality. I had to make sounds to feel sane. My heart felt raw and wounded.

During this time I visited a Buddhist monastery and there I sounded out prayers to help Amanda with her transition and her journey of transformation. I felt Amanda's presence. As I was sounding the intention of love and peace, I heard a flute playing in my mind. Together we orchestrated and composed a soundscape like no other I have experienced. It was pure magic. Deeper and deeper I immersed myself. I felt every cell of my being become sound. I was no longer flesh. My whole body was vibrating to a new frequency. The sounds were so ancient, from a time unknown to me. Time had ceased. I had opened up a new dimension within myself. In this altered state, I caught a glimpse of the possibility of travelling through multi-dimensions. Incredible! Tears were streaming down my face as the sounds filled my universe with loving ecstasy. Through the gift of sound, I discovered an overwhelmingly profound sense of gratitude, acceptance, forgiveness and liberation for all that is. Thank God for sound.

~ **Debi Lloyd, New Zealand**

Support and oneness

A little while ago my dad had to undergo heart surgery, which was complicated by the fact that he also has Parkinson's disease. I struggled with asking for assistance, but the moment I broke through the resistance, my sound tribe was there, supporting me with messages of love and strength. During Dad's operation, I sounded with all my heart. I felt the sounds of my Soul Voice colleagues join me, as I felt an incredible surge of strength and clarity of intention and love. I received many messages and had a deepening sense of the healing that was occurring as he had his heart 'fixed'. The male ancestral line was very present and I felt their support flow through as Dad received blessings, understanding, forgiveness and love.

Looking up, I saw three white doves circling the building. Dad went on to make an amazingly speedy recovery, to the astonishment of the medical team. The sounds had shifted something very profound for me too. The heavy burden I felt I had long been carrying felt lighter. I no longer felt alone or separated, but deeply connected on many levels: to my ancestral line, to my tribe, to a greater sense of oneness with divinity and the vast supportive network that exists at all times, ever flowing and vibrating in the ether, waiting to be received.

Our voices had joined in unison and had connected and intensified our intentions, reaching far beyond time and place, back into history, shifting and unblocking the resonance of withheld energy.

My experience on that day showed me that separation is just an illusion that comes from the patterns of our humanness and our history, both collectively and individually.

By surrendering and connecting to the collective vibrations of sound, we have the opportunity to heal deeply as we connect to a unified field far greater than us. Through this, we come home to ourselves and our core. That day was a day of receiving unexpected gifts, on many levels.

~ Caroline Barnes, United Kingdom

References

Michael Bernard Beckwith, *Life Visioning*, Sounds True 2012

Chip Conley, *Emotional Equations*, Simon & Schuster 2012

Wayne Dyer, *The Power of Intention*, Hay House 2004,
www.hayhouse.com.au

Kristin Flood, *The Francis Factor*, Stenersens 2011

Kahlil Gibran, *The Prophet*, Wordsworth Editions 1996

Peter Grunwald, *Eyebody*, Condevis 2008

Hans Jenny, *Cymatics: A Study of Wave Phenomena and Vibration*,
MACROmedia 2001, www.cymaticsource.com

Laurel Elizabeth Keyes, *Toning: The Creative Power of the Voice*,
De Vorss & Co 1990

Roy Levine, *Waking the Tiger*, North Atlantic 1997

Candace Pert, *Molecules of Emotions*, Scribner 1997

Gabrielle Roth, *Maps to Ecstasy*, New World Library 1998

Martina Roy, *Emotional Balance*, Hay House 2011

Makuini Ruth Tai, *Te Waihanga: The Creative Waters,* Wenetia
1995, www.arohainsights.com

Alfred Tomatis, *The Conscious Ear*, Station Hill 1991

Expression into Freedom Instructional CD

Speaking voice: Karina Schelde
Sound engineering: Kevin Clark
Sounding: Karina (Track 1 Kevin & Karina)

Track 1: Introduction

Welcome to the *Expression into Freedom* CD. The voice is a beautiful expression of who we truly are, and reflects our inner universe. Each word we express sends out a vibrational imprint so explore these exercises with an open heart, be gentle and acknowledge yourself each time you practise. **Be passionate about your progress and let the sound itself guide you on your unique journey.**

Enjoy becoming more spontaneous, authentic and free in your various creative expressions. Let go of judging your voice in order to discover that each expression indeed carries its own message for you. Simply listen within and feel.

Let your voice soar to its potential and let it show you the way: *If you have a voice, you can sound!* I support and hold you in a safe space of trust, so you may have the courage to persevere. I invite you to be inspired and stay embraced by the powerful Soul Voice medicine.

This CD may be listened to in your own rhythm; most likely you will choose only a couple of exercises each time you practise. You may do the exercises in the designated time frame, or, if you wish, you may turn off the CD and practise at your own pace. At the beginning of tracks I will give you a short demonstration of how I might approach the exercise. There are five minutes of silence at the end of each instruction, which allows you to practise on your own.

Track 2: The full deep breath and the opening *ah*-sound

Breath is a fundamental ingredient for the human voice. Conscious breathing is an invitation to say yes to life and a genuine way of celebrating it. A full deep breath is energising and relaxing and will progressively lead to a richer resonance when you sound. Furthermore this practice with the opening *ah*-sound will start to free your vocal expression.

» Get into a comfortable body position lying on your back and relax. Become conscious of how you breathe.

» Now let your mouth be wide open, so that the breath can move freely through it for both the inhale and the exhale. Now, start to exaggerate your breathing with full deep breath and observe your body's response to this open mouth breathing. Make the inhale and the exhale of almost equal length. Begin this practice now as I continue the instruction.

» Put your hands on your stomach area and take some deep breaths to observe its movements. On the inhale allow your stomach muscles to expand. You may also observe subtle movements in the pelvis area. Practise this several times and for each inhaling breath let your hands move upwards and outwards.

» On the exhale relax and let the stomach return to normal. Surrender.

» Let's do this breathing practice together a couple of times with attention to the stomach muscles ...

» The next step is to use the abdominal muscles situated around the ribcage. Put your hands on your ribcage and expand this area on the inhale. Check your hands are being moved by the breath and relax on the exhale and surrender.

» Let's do this breathing practice together a couple of times with attention to the abdominal muscles ...

» The next step is to use the chest muscles, which lifts the upper part of the ribcage. Fill your lungs and remember the full open mouth breathing. Put your hands on the chest muscles and let them be moved by the breath. Relax on the exhale and surrender.

» Let's do this breathing practice together a couple of times with attention to the chest muscles …

» The final round is to combine all the muscle groups of the stomach, abdomen and chest in this deep breathing exercise. Let each area expand on a deep inhaling breath and then return to normal on a relaxed exhaling breath. Remember to keep your mouth wide open on both the inhale as well as the exhale and allow them to be of almost equal length.

» Let's do this breathing practice together a couple of times …

» You are now ready to make an opening *ah*-sound. Take a deep inhaling breath with a wide open mouth and then hold your breath for a second, before you exhale slowly making a long sustaining *ah*-sound still with wide open mouth. Do not control the sound, but allow it to fluctuate naturally. Feel the sound and let go of wanting to stay on pitch. You cannot do it wrong so trust what wants to be expressed through you.

» Let's do it together a couple of times …

» For the next five minutes there will be silence in order for you to further practise 'The full deep breath and the opening *ah*-sound.'

» Now slowly bring yourself back as you become aware of your breathing.

» Contact your feet and feel the ground. Be still. Take time to integrate. Trust your discoveries and the insights you may have had during this journey.

Track 3: Feeling is healing

Emotions are our guides to living life fully. Invite yourself to become more alive by exploring them. The 'Feeling is healing' exercise is an experience of listening to the body sensations, feeling them and nurturing them with sound. It is a simple, yet an effective practice. Let yourself be surprised.

» Get into a comfortable body position, as you consciously observe your breath. Contact that part of your body where you feel something, either it's a pleasant sensation, or one of discomfort or pain. Take a moment to locate that area now.

» Before you start the experience remember that if you are not able to feel anything or are in contact with any form of judgment or resistance, simply *play with* sounding an emotion.

» Trust the area you have chosen and simply make sounds as to what you feel. Put your hands on the area if you wish. Exaggerate the sounds which will allow the emotion to be heightened. Let one sound guide you to the next sound and so on. Listen.

» Name aloud any feeling and then sound it. Trust your intuition.

» For the next five minutes there will be silence in order for you to further practise 'Feeling is healing.'

» Complete your process with some soothing sounds now.

» Slowly and gently come back to your breath. Contact your feet and feel the ground. Take time to relax and listen in order to integrate this process and let the new awareness of your feeling body reveal its wisdom to you. Trust and accept.

Track 4: The primal animal within

The reptilian brain connects us to our instincts and our primal expressions. When we awaken these we access a stronger sensuality and groundedness to set healthier boundaries. Be playful and adventurous in this practice and let your primal nature guide you.

» Sit in a comfortable position and start by making *ah*-sounds or sighing sounds. Let's do it together now …

» Connect to the lower part of your body in your chi-area which is a couple of centimeters below your navel. Move gently into an all-fours position. This is the area where your instinctive primal sounds will originate. You will make some guttural and growling sounds like this …

» You may sound like a lion or a tiger or any other animal that has some kind of growling sounds.

» Allow the body to move and be an extension of the sounding process. Play and listen to the sound itself as it will guide you when you do so; let your animal nature play. Use your imagination to explore the animal's natural activities and have fun.

» For the next five minutes there will be silence in order for you to further practise 'The primal animal within.'

» Start to make a gentle transition back by paying attention to your breath. Be in silence for a moment. Receive insights as to what it means to be in your instinctive power and alertness. Listen to your heart.

Track 5: Grief released

Grief is such a big healer. It teaches you to let go as no other emotion can. Surrender and let grief soften your hard edges and any resistance or hurtful memories you may have. Let grief assist you to restore peace, balance and forgiveness.

» Choose a comfortable body position. Be still and take some deep breaths with sighing or *ah*-sounds. Let's do that together now …

» Place your face in your hands and start to gently massage it as you continue to listen to my instructions. In a moment you will begin to make some gentle sounds that imitate what grief and sadness may be for you. By listening you will progressively access memories that may invite or provoke grief.

» Is it disappointment that gets you down? Is it old hurt feelings of abandonment or abuse from the past? Is it a sense of not succeeding and doing what you really wish to do? Is it a lack of passion and fullheartedness in your endeavours?

Feel where the grief resides and then let the sounds originate from that area.

» Be courageous and let grief nurture your soul. Remember to *play* with the energy if you get stuck. Surrender and stay open to the sounds that want to be expressed through you. Start with some gentle sounds now at first.

» For the next five minutes there will be silence in order for you to further release and explore grief and sadness.

» Start to slowly complete now, as you send soothing harmonious *ah*-sounds to the areas in your body you have been working with. I will do it with you …

» Now, give space and time to complete your grief process by entering into silence when you are ready. Dwell in gratitude and forgiveness for an extended time to integrate.

Track 6: Who am I?

Experiencing your self-expression brings great joy and freedom. In this practice you will be challenged as far as you are willing to go with yourself! Take action to move whatever frightens you, shakes you, ignites you, challenges you!

» Celebrate your uniqueness and let your world be a better place to live because you have made this commitment.

» Place yourself in front of a mirror where you are able to see most of your body. Gaze into the mirror and observe your face, its contours and expressions. Now start to make funny faces and sounds, as if you were massaging your face with your expressions. Do this as I continue the instructions.

» Let these expressions include your entire body. Continue to play and release anything that surfaces. Be creative and use your inner child's imagination.

» You may at any time move away from the mirror in order to move freely. Use the mirror when you are lost or whenever it serves you.

» Now check you are in contact with your chi-centre a couple of centimeters below the navel. Start to feel from this area.

Experiment fullheartedly. Forget about yourself as you express anything that is unfamiliar, makes you laugh, cry or jump with sheer excitement.

» Who are you and who do you wish to show to the world?
» Choose any character you wish and be this persona one hundred percent. Own it completely and say yes to your unique expression. Identify fully with your chosen character and improvise anything that arises from your heart, chi-centre or other parts of your body. Exaggerate all expressions, be they movements, words, sounds or emotions. Allow your passion to express more of yourself than you have ever dared to do.
» Don't hide. Be heard and be seen for who you are. Express that which you fear the most. It is when your heart beats faster that you stop expressing your habitual self. Wake up your dormant self. Feel your feelings. Now express even more that which is scary and that which puts you on the edge. Own it, be it, express the extreme, go for it!
» For the next five minutes there will be silence in order for you to further explore the 'Who am I?'
» Come back slowly. Cease your creative expressions and let your emotions calm down. Become aware of your breath. Acknowledge yourself for the challenging steps you took and forgive yourself for where you did not go. Feel this warm embrace. Listen and be still. Lay down and relax completely for an extended time.

Track 7: The intuitive flow of sound and movement

When we move through life with a relaxed ease and grace and a surrendering attitude we experience life coming towards us. So let this practice bring you to more authentic communication and expression, as you refine your ability to move according to your creative impulses.

» This exercise requires being barefoot. Find a place where you can move freely and sound loudly. Now start to move in slow motion by stretching your body as I continue the instructions.

» By slowing down the movement you will become more conscious and alert. You will then also be able to put attention to the placement of your feet: in this moment I ask you to make an effort to separate your toes from one another, so that they individually touch the ground. This brings a much stronger connection to the earth and therefore greater grounding.

» Pause. Now you are ready to add sounds to your movement. Look at the sound as an extension of your movement and surprise yourself!

» For each movement there is a sound expression and for each sound there is a movement expression. Move with certainty.

» Any time you feel unsure, focus on your individual toes touching the ground. Give space and time. Let the exercise bring you satisfaction and effortlessness. Surrender to the flow in joy.

» For the next five minutes there will be silence in order for you to further explore 'the intuitive flow of sound and movement.'

» Now slowly move to a completion and come into stillness. Lay down to relax. See yourself in time and space, in movement and expression, in excellence. You cannot do it wrong, you can only come closer and closer to your essence which directs you and gives you the spark of life; that which never leaves you. Your inner voice, your divine connection to all that is.

*Thank you for letting me be a part
of your Soul Voice journey.
It is my hope that you will
continue to explore your
unique and beautiful voice,
with wonder, passion and gratitude.
In sacred loving resonance …*

Books and CDs by Karina Schelde

BOOKS
The Magic Power of the Human Voice
Expression into Freedom
Soul Voice

AUDIO BOOK
Expression into Freedom

SOUND HEALING CDS
Chakra Sound Healing & Heart Songs
The Song of the Soul

For information on Soul Voice® workshops and
Practitioners' Certification Programme, or to order products, contact us at:

www.soulvoice.net | admin@soulvoice.net

Soul Voice International
PO Box 384
Whitianga 3542
New Zealand